October, 2003

Dear Max,

To the best scrub nurse a young doctor could have ever wished for - if I could have only moved you back to Louisiana!

Love,

Jeffrey

the beauty makers

C.C. RISENHOOVER
& DON PATTERSON

Kiamichi House

Also by C.C. Risenhoover

DEAD EVEN
BLOOD BATH
CHILD STALKER
DEATH ANGEL
LETHAL RAGE
TRESTLES OVER DARKNESS
WINE, MURDER & BLUEBERRY SUNDAES
MURDER AT THE FINAL FOUR
OUTSIDE THE LINES
SATAN'S MARK
WHITE HEAT
HAPPY BIRTHDAY JESUS
LARRY HAGMAN
TECHNIQUES OF GREAT
BASS FISHERMEN

Printed in the United States of America

FIRST EDITION

Library of Congress Cataloging-in-Publication Data

Risenhoover, C.C.
The Beauty Makers / C.C. Risenhoover. – 1st ed.
p. cm.
ISBN 1-930899-10-6
LCCN 2003092511

AUTHOR'S NOTE

Information about the doctors profiled in this book was provided to the authors and editors individually by those self same doctors, and does not represent an endorsement by the publisher, authors and editors.

DESIGN BY JEFF STANTON

Published by Kiamichi House, an imprint of Brazos Currents Worldwide

To Dedicated Physicians,
whose interest in their Patients
supercedes all else

the beauty makers
DR. E. GAYLON MCCOLLOUGH
350 Cypress Bend Drive
Gulf Shores, Alabama 36542
(251) 967-7000

Dr. Gaylon McCollough

ad he made different choices in life, Dr. E. Gaylon McCollough might well have been a top player in the National Football League as well as an internationally recognized surgeon who has taught the art and science of facial plastic surgery and Rejuvenology™ to physicians around the world.

After a sterling college career playing for Bear Bryant at the University of Alabama, which included a national championship, he was drafted by the NFL Dallas Cowboys and offered an exceptional bonus for the times. He seriously considered playing while going to medical school, but a doctor from Alabama advised him to go straight into school.

It was not an easy choice for a young man who had been Joe Namath's center, who married Alabama's beauty queen in his senior year, and who was going to have to work his way through medical school. The bonus money would have made medical school a lot easier.

"Even if I had played in the NFL," he said, "there was never any doubt that I would be going to medical school."

Neither medical school nor the University of Alabama had been in his earlier plans. Following a high school football championship at Enterprise, Alabama, the highly recruited young athlete had planned to enroll at Georgia Tech to play football and study architecture. But along came Coach Bryant with an offer he couldn't refuse – "Come to Alabama and I'll promise you a national championship."

Few high school football players could say no to Coach Bryant, especially if you were from Alabama.

"I had wanted to be an architect because my dad was in the construction business and I had worked in construction," Dr.

McCollough said. "It's what I knew. But the University of Alabama didn't have an architectural program, so I was pushed in a different direction."

As to why he selected facial plastic surgery as a specialty, a lecture by a plastic surgeon during his second year of medical school caused him to investigate the field as a specialty.

"I saw it as architectural medicine," he said, "so I started learning all about it. From the time I was a small boy I had been enamored with faces...loved to draw faces. So that's the route I chose...plastic surgery of the face."

During his junior year of medical school, football once again enticed him. The Atlanta Falcons had a farm team, so, "after hours and weekends," he played a year in a league against the farm teams of other NFL teams and made "all pro."

"It was a good farm system," he said, "it was a better job than working as an orderly at a community hospital to pay the bills of medical school and my family, but emotionally I was out of football. I had a wife, a three-year-old son and had made a commitment to excel in medicine."

The Gulf Shores, Alabama-based surgeon practices at the McCollough Institute for Appearance and Health, a thirty-two thousand square foot personal enhancement center located in the heart of Craft Farms Coastal Golf Resort.

But he has never been provincial. He has taught in Australia, Canada, Columbia, England, Switzerland, The Netherlands, Germany, India, Italy, Mexico, Peru, South Africa, Spain and Turkey.

"Clearly, destiny has a way of putting us in the right place...at the right time," he said. "Since relocating to Gulf Shores, and while maintaining a fulltime facial plastic surgery practice, I've been able to build a world-class human enhancement center, dedicated to helping people look, feel and perform better...longer. Now, we're ready to share our "Rejuvenology™" experiences and programs with professionals around the world"

Dr. McCollough founded the first McCollough Plastic Surgery

Clinic in Birmingham, Alabama in nineteen seventy-four, but sold it in the nineteen nineties and moved his practice to Gulf Shores.

"Shortly after selling the clinic in Birmingham, it became clear that the new owners' agendas differed from that I had used to create the paradigm they purchased," he said. "So I chose to set out on my own and do it again, only this time to make it bigger and better. And my research showed that the best place to do it was Gulf Shores, a beachside golf resort on the southernmost tip of Alabama at the Gulf of Mexico."

The doctor said he had intended that the programs, professionals and facilities at the new institute surpass anything with which he had previously been affiliated – and that he had not been disappointed.

"I don't think there is anything comparable to it anywhere," he said. "It's thoughtfully tucked among the lakes and fairways of the Arnold Palmer-designed Cypress Bend Course at Craft Farms Coastal Golf Resort. It's a perfect setting for bringing nature and science together to enhance the quality and length of people's lives. The data is conclusive. If you take better care of yourself, you will be rewarded for your effort."

In addition to Dr. McCollough's facial and nasal plastic surgery practice, the institute offers total body cosmetic and reconstructive surgery, cranio-facial surgery and hair transplantation, by Dr. Jack A. Davidson. Dr. A. Dex Dunavent operates the general, implant and cosmetic dentistry clinic, and Dr. Larry Brock is in charge of the institute's Health and Longevity Center.

"The Health and Longevity Center offers virtual physical examinations," said Dr. McCollough, "and our non-invasive studies of the heart and body are achieved with the latest three-dimensional EBT body scanner. The Imatron scanner, under direction of Dr. Brock and his staff, provides newer and more advanced ways for clients to learn about their bodies. Most important, perhaps, clients are shown how to participate with their doctors and advisers in a new kind of partnership for achieving better health. We are not in competition with other doctors and community hospitals. By detecting problems before symptoms arise, we can send patients for treatment early in the disease process."

The doctor said that for heightened performance and vitality the institute has opened the world's first "Rejuvenology™ Center, which offers a scientific nutritional and hormonal supplement program for men and women of all ages. Replacement therapy after menopause (for women) and andropause (for men) is formulated and dispensed from Dr. David Rothbardt's compounding pharmacy.

"We also offer personalized weight management and fitness training in Tony Kennon's Forever Young Center," he said, "and the Med-Spa and Skin Care Center's professionals offer treatments and enhancement services beyond those available in most spas.

"The institute offers something for health and appearance conscious people of every age...and for every budget."

Dr. McCollough said the institute is all about lifting spirits and shaping bodies – for both women and men.

"By emphasizing preventive maintenance and early detection, we can assist patients and their physicians with a balanced approach to better health," he said. "With our individual and group health and appearance retreats, we're able to combine pleasure with everyone's objective to look and feel better.

Executives and professionals leave the retreat with a better understanding of how to take better care of themselves...and those they serve.

"There's definitely a void in the system because the medical profession spends much time treating disease after it has occurred and not enough time on prevention. The focus in medical school, unfortunately, is on disease, not prevention. Our objective at the institute, on the other hand, is the total person...mind, body and soul. So we bring together the positive aspects of looking better, feeling better and living longer. A person is capable of living a hundred to one hundred twenty-five years, depending on his or her decisions. But anything in excess takes years away from us."

Once the McCollough Institute for Appearance and Health

was completed, the doctor embarked on the second phase of his plan. He established the American College of Rejuvenology™ and its instructional arm, the annual World Congress on Optimal Appearance and Health (Rejuvenology™) so that doctors from around the world could gather at the Gulf Coast to share information and develop better ways to care for patients.

While Dr. McCollough's practice is limited to plastic surgery of the face and nose, he emphasizes that, today, patients expect their doctors to know about trends in the scientific revolution of health care. Patients have greater access to information and are learning that, with a healthy lifestyle, they can reduce the likelihood of contracting disease, live longer, and look better. "However," the doctor added, "People want more than the absence of disease. They want a chance to find health with doctors they already trust."

Dr. McCollough believes that although "health" is the apparent objective, "looking better" is the driving force behind self-help programs, many of which assist individuals maintain their weight, tone their bodies, eat healthier diets, take vitamins, minerals, and herbs, and replace disappearing hormones.

The problem, McCollough emphasizes, is that although a growing percentage of the population wants to include health and longevity protocols in their lifestyle, no existing specialty offers both surgical and medical appearance and health enhancement in its educational curriculum, so most doctors do not include pro-active programs in their practices. Patients don't know where to go, or whom to consult for optimal health and appearance counseling.

To help solve the dilemma, Dr. McCollough organized the first World Congress for Optimal Appearance and Health (Rejuvenology™) in Gulf Shores, Alabama, March 13-16, 2003 and established a new specialty, which fills the void. The American College of Rejuvenology™ is a multi-disciplinary association of doctors and surgeons pursuing a common goal—optimal health and appearance.

"Rejuvenology™" (as defined by Dr. McCollough) is the pro-active art and science of appearance and health enhancement...for men and women...of all ages, with averting preventable disease and premature aging as objectives to be achieved through life-style and behavior modification...with, and without surgery and prescription medications and therapy."

"The educational and instructional programs of the non-profit American College of Rejuvenology™ are steps in the right direction," Dr. McCollough stressed. "Around the world, people are seeking "mainstream" doctors and surgeons, who advocate preventing disease...finding health...and improving appearance...all at the same time," he said. "The logical doctor to provide comprehensive Rejuvenology™ is the doctor, who the patient trusts to improve his or her appearance. It's simply a matter of expanding medical education and incorporating outcome-based scientific protocols."

Dr. McCollough added, "While, The Fountain of Youth is not, yet, ours to offer, the time-tested elixirs of good fortune...optimal health and beauty...are very near...and these can be had when doctors and patients work together to combat the undesirable signs and symptoms of premature aging and its undesirable consequences. Some of the most common and avoidable diseases are influenced by behavioral modification. Unquestionably, obesity and stress take away from one's appearance, sense of well being, and life span. Yet, throughout our society, each is growing in epidemic proportions, erasing beauty or handsomeness from their paths. And, doctors need to focus as much on prevention of disease as vigorously as on treatment. I know that for the rest of my professional career, I will be engaged in the endless pursuit of ways to help people look better, feel better, perform better...and live longer. We will take the experiences of the McCollough Institute in Gulf Shores and share it will our medical and surgical colleagues through the American College of Rejuvenology™ and its educational arms."

Gulf Shores architect Sted McCollough, the doctor's son, designed the institute, and helped his father's vision become a reality. Dr. and Mrs. McCollough (former Miss Alabama, Susan Nomberg) also have a daughter, Chanee, who is married to an Andalusia, Alabama attorney.

"The McCollough Institute's neo-classical style artfully reflects a balance of form and function," the doctor said. "Patient comfort and confidentiality were addressed to ensure a modern, yet non-institutional, ambiance, carried into the private villas, which guests can reserve for a day, week or longer. Our on-site concierge assists guests in planning their activities.

"The interiors of the institute were coordinated by my wife, Susan. And they surpass the work she did on our previous clinics in Birmingham. Those facilities achieved international acclaim for their 'five-star' standards and avant-garde style. Already resort developers from at least three other states have contacted us about duplicating the Gulf Shores Institute in their resorts."

The doctor said he has always been motivated by opportunity...by recognizing a need and trying to fill it to the best of his ability.

"As an athlete," said McCollough, "I was trained to be the very best I could best...every day. Each year, we sought the National Championship. In 1964, we achieved that objective. Now, as a physician, surgeon, and scientist, I am, still driven by a sense of accomplishment, by wanting to be the best in my profession and help others provide a better quality of life for those we serve."

The doctor said his work is his recreation, but that he also loves to write and usually begins penning his thoughts at five-thirty to six-o'clock in the morning, before going to the Institute. He occasionally escapes to his farm—actually a wildlife preserve— near his hometown.

"We raise trees, turkeys, deer, squirrels, rabbits, and fish in the lake we built on the property," he said. "There is also a stable of three horses. "I do my best thinking while riding those horses through the woods and fields of our farm," the doctor said.

Dr. McCollough, certified by the American Board of Facial Plastic and Reconstructive Surgery and the American Board of Otolaryngology, is included in Woodward and White's Best Doctors in America and in the National Registry of Who's Who. He has also authored three major textbooks on facial and nasal plastic surgery, numerous peer reviewed medical publications and directed a score of post-graduate instructional seminars for doctors from around the world.

In addition to receiving his undergraduate degree with honors from the University of Alabama, he was also named to the Academic All-America Football Team the same year. He also received the Frank Thomas Award for Scholastics and Athletics and the Charlie Compton Award for Citizenship and Stewardship while an undergraduate. Thirty years later, he received the All-American Football Foundation's "Unsung Hero" Award.

He received his MD degree from the University of Alabama Medical School and, following residency training at the University of Alabama and Tulane University, completed an approved program of specialized training in facial plastic surgery in Beverly Hills, California; New Orleans, Louisiana and Boston, Massachusetts.

"I was fortunate to be trained by the best in their fields," the doctor said.

In his books, **SHOULDERS OF GIANTS** and **BEFORE AND AFTER**, McCollough gave much of the credit for his success to the "Giants" in their professions, who, as he pursued his own goals, allowed him to climb upon their shoulders to see farther...and more distantly.

Dr. McCollough was elected as the American Board of Facial Plastic and Reconstructive Surgery's first president. He also served as president of the American Association of Cosmetic Surgeons and the American Academy of Facial Plastic and Reconstructive Surgery, Inc. and in nineteen eighty-five, was inducted into the American Board of Cosmetic Surgery as an honorary member.

He is a clinical professor in the Department of Surgery at the University of Alabama-Birmingham, a clinical instructor at Faulkner State Community College and is a member of numerous professional associations. Honors include being named to the Alabama Senior Citizens Hall of Fame and Alabama Citizen of the Year.

The doctor has served as Vice Chairman of the University of

Dr. E. Gaylon McCollough

Alabama President's Cabinet, Chairman of the Board of the First & Ten Club of Alabama, President of the Board of Directors of the Alabama Sports Hall of Fame and President of the Birmingham Touchdown Club. He also served as a director of the Better Business Bureau, South Baldwin Hospital Foundation and Chairman of the Alabama Special Olympics Medical Advisory Board.

the beauty makers
DR. PEARLMAN D. HICKS, JR.
436 North Bedford Drive #300
Beverly Hills, California 90210
(310) 652-9312

Dr. Pearlman D. Hicks Jr.

Dr. Pearlman D. Hicks Jr. said he chose plastic surgery because "it is the only specialty in medicine where you can be creative and where each patient's problem is different. You have to devise a solution for each problem because everybody's problem is different."

The Beverly Hills, California – based surgeon also said he thought his expertise in the care of people of color – African Americans and others of different ethnic backgrounds – set him apart from other physicians in his field of specialization.

"A professor once told me that when you are operating on a patient, you should operate as if she was your mother and not your mother-in-law," he said, laughing. To this day I keep that advice in mind when caring for a patient. I treat every patient as if she or he is a member of my family."

Dr. Hicks said he aspired to being a doctor at an early age, and had wanted to be a plastic surgeon since working at the Massachusetts Eye and Ear Infirmary in Boston. His reason for being at the infirmary, oddly enough, was the result of a football injury to his ankle.

"I was born in Hamilton, Ohio, which is a small farming town twenty-five miles north of Cincinnati," he said. "I attended schools in Ohio, was captain of my high school football team, class president, Honor Society president and valedictorian of my class.

"I went to Harvard University following graduation from high school and played varsity football there for two years. At one time I held the record for the most touchdowns scored by a freshman, but an injury to my ankle forced me to give up football during my junior year."

Prior to the injury the doctor had been working part-time at Boys' Clubs of Boston to help subsidize his education, but after giving up football he took a part-time job as a research assistant at the Massachusetts Eye and Ear Infirmary at Massachusetts General Hospital – which is where his interest in plastic surgery grew.

"Being the best you can be as a plastic surgeon requires a strong work ethic and the desire to never stop learning," Dr. Hicks said, "and I've always had that. My first job when a kid was as a newspaper delivery boy, and my second was as a bag boy for an A&P Supermarket. I was actually promoted to assistant produce manager of the A&P before going to college.

"My high school teachers and football coaches were major influences in my life. They encouraged me to go to college instead of working in the steel mill, which most of the kids in the area did after graduating high school."

The doctor's professional background includes being chief surgical resident at Case Western Reserve School of Medicine, chief plastic surgical resident at Peter Bent Brigham Hospital in Boston and chief plastic surgical resident at the Boston Children's Hospital. He began practicing in California in nineteen seventy-nine.

"A person planning plastic surgery should carefully research the doctor she or he is considering," Dr. Hicks said. "You need to make sure the doctor is board certified in plastic and reconstructive surgery. Plastic and reconstructive surgeons, unlike other facial surgical specialties, require a full seven years of training...including five years of general surgery."

The doctor said a patient should make every possible effort to be in the best health possible before surgery.

"That means eliminating unhealthy habits such as smoking, drinking and taking medicines not prescribed by a physician," he said. "They also need to avoid these unhealthy habits after surgery, and to exercise and try to stay in good shape to improve the overall results of the surgery."

Dr. Hicks said he felt a woman's beauty is most enhanced by the proportion of her cheeks, chin, nose and eyes as they relate to the rest of her face.

Dr. Pearlman D. Hicks Jr.

"Nice cheeks that are not too flat are very appealing," he said. "The color of the skin and the tone of the skin are also very important, whether the patient is African American, Caucasian or Asian. A healthy woman's skin has a vibrant, rosy appearance."

The doctor said reconstructive cases are by far the most difficult for a plastic surgeon, especially when the patient has been involved in a severe accident.

"One of my patients had third degree burns over her face, neck and upper body," he said. "Her ears, nose and lips were severely burned, so it took several years of reconstruction to get her back to normal.

"Another patient was born without a nose and had a severe congenital deformity with a large cleft going from her upper lip into her face and between her eyes. It took a great deal of reconstructive work to give her a nose and normal looking face, but handling surgeries of this nature is what makes my job rewarding."

Dr. Hicks was voted one of the best surgeons in the country by **Guide to Top Doctors** magazine. For his service as a reconstructive plastic surgeon to inner city people in Los Angeles California, he was also honored by the LA city council.

He has appeared on numerous TV shows, such as Oprah Winfrey and Hard Copy, and has been interviewed for stories by ABC, CBS, NBC, Nuevo, the **Los Angeles Times** and by **Ebony**, **Essence** and **Jet** magazines.

"I'm a member of the California State Boxing Commission," he said. "I'm one of the fight doctors, attend all the major fights in California as well as some in Las Vegas. I have a large number of boxers who are patients.

"My hobbies are jogging, swimming, camping, skiing and scuba diving. When I go on vacation, I always try to include scuba diving in my activities."

the beauty makers
DR. MARK GILLILAND, M.D.
6624 Fannin – Suite 2260
Houston, Texas 77030
(713) 799-8885

Dr. Mark D. Gilliland

Dr. Mark D. Gilliland, M.D., FACS, FICS, is a Houston-based board certified plastic surgeon devoted to the art and science of the field. His focus in aesthetic plastic surgery is exclusively devoted to facial rejuvenation and body contouring, including breast surgery.

"No plastic surgeon can be an expert in all areas of plastic surgery," he says. "The field simply moves too quickly.

"For the patient, the principal factor for success in plastic surgery is the selection of the plastic surgeon. Any medical doctor can perform such surgery, but not always with the desired results. Unfortunately, the consumer cannot always immediately detect which surgeon has the experience and knowledge to create the look he or she desires.

"My primary concern in doing plastic surgery is, and always will be, patient safety, minimizing risk and maximizing the quality of the result. The patient's general health, healing ability and skin condition all influence the quality of results. I encourage a person to communicate her or his goals during consultation. A patient's active participation is a key factor in the outcome of their surgery."

That the doctor is so concerned about the welfare of his patients comes as no surprise to those who know him. He is a perfectionist, always studying and striving to improve, even in areas where he is considered an authority and expert.

High school valedictorian at New Mexico Military Institute in Roswell, magna cum laude graduate at the University of Kansas (microbiology), and among the top ten percent of his medical school class are typical examples of the academic excellence he demands of himself. His graduate thesis describing the cellular mechanisms of aging exemplified his devotion to furthering aesthetic female beauty and male attractiveness long past middle age, a goal he still pursues.

Dr. Gilliland's interest in surgery brought him to the University of Texas at the Texas Medical Center in Houston in nineteen seventy-seven, where he spent five years in general surgery with famed Drs. Denton Cooley, Red Duke, and the surgical oncologists at M.D. Anderson Hospital. He then pursued aesthetic plastic surgery at UCLA in Los Angeles, where the emphasis was on the finer details of cosmetic surgery.

The doctor has performed more than twenty thousand procedures, experience that contributes to intangible surgical judgment and the ability to go the extra mile pursuing the optimum cosmetic result while minimizing risks. Every procedure has a risk/benefit ratio best determined by the individual surgeon's experience.

Some of his intellectual and technical contributions to the field of plastic surgery include:

• Pioneering tumescent infiltration and ultrasonic assisted liposuction for major body reshaping under general anesthesia, a technique allowing the safe removal of more fat at one sitting, enhanced cosmetic result and diminished postoperative bruising and swelling.

• Performing the first "abdominal etching" and "modified abdominal etching" techniques and presenting the results on abdominal liposculpture in nineteen ninety-three. Physicians worldwide have attempted to simulate these procedures. These techniques create the "six-pack" look in fit individuals by carefully removing the superficial fat to enhance the natural topography of underlying abdominal muscles.

• Developing CAST (Circumferential Para-Axillary Superficial Tumescent) liposuction of the arms, a procedure that improves the sagging arms skin that may cause a middle-age woman not to wear a sleeveless dress. Early treatment can prevent the development of "batwing deformity" commonly seen in elderly individuals. For arms with severe laxity, the standard treatment is cutting out the extra skin along the inside of the arm and down to the elbow (brachioplasty). This long scar is very noticeable and undesirable. CAST liposuction, plus a small armpit scar (minibrachioplasty) frequently creates an equal improvement in arm contour without the long scar.

• Co-authoring the largest published series in the world on safety issues in ultrasonic assisted large volume liposuction (seven hundred sixty-six patients with a one point seven percent complication rate), maximizing the cosmetic result in large volume liposuction (over twenty pounds of fat removed). This experience, removing large fat volumes, can create dramatic changes. The most significant change was a patient who went from a size twenty-two to a size twelve. Additional metabolic benefits include lowering of blood pressure and blood glucose.

• Being one of the first plastic surgeons in the United States to be appointed to the National Task Force for Liposuction Safety by the American Society of Plastic Surgeons.

• Being the first plastic surgeon to present a large series of patients demonstrating the synergistic combination of ultrasonic energy and body lifting (Ultrasonic Body Lift) for cosmetic enhancement of patients with excess skin and fat. This procedure makes the body more shapely, thinner, and younger by reducing cellulite.

The list of his accomplishments and contributions goes on and on, evidence that he is considered "leading edge" and "special" in his field. Further evidence of his reputation is the fact that patients come to him in Houston from California, New York, Florida and many other states, along with international clientele from many countries. In two thousand two he traveled to the Middle East to operate on members of the royal family in Saudi Arabia.

Because of Dr. Gilliland's success in combining art and science in cosmetic surgery, along with his ability to enhance the cosmetic result while promoting safety, he has been featured speaker for numerous national and international plastic surgery conferences. They include the American Society for Aesthetic Plastic Surgery, the International Society of Aesthetic Plastic Surgery, The Lipoplasty Society, and the American Society of Plastic and Reconstructive Surgery.

A lecturer at plastic surgery symposia worldwide, he has delivered more than seventy-five scientific presentations in numerous countries, including Australia, Brazil, Canada, France, Mexico, and Zimbabwe, South Africa. He has also published more than forty scientific abstracts, articles and book chapters on plastic surgery.

In addition, the doctor has been interviewed and quoted in such magazines as **Allure** and **Vogue**; by numerous newspapers, including the **Wall Street Journal**; and on NBC News and ABC News broadcasts. Indeed, the large array of print and electronic media seeking his expertise over the years are too numerous to mention.

While Dr. Gilliland fields many questions about a variety of plastic surgery procedures, there is tremendous interest in Body Lift, which is the same as Circumferential Abdominoplasty. In this procedure the doctor utilizes ultrasonic energy to easily remove fat and enhance skin retraction. The four- to six-hour procedure requires general anesthesia, a one- to two-day hospital stay, and a three- to four-week recovery period. The doctor has never had to give a blood transfusion, so there is no need for autogenous blood donation. He concentrates on the area that most bothers the patient: abdomen, inner/anterior thigh, buttocks/outer thigh and back.

Body lifting is similar to face lifting. With a facelift the sagging skin and wrinkles of the face are lifted and the scar hidden in the hair. With a body lift the sagging skin of the thighs and buttocks is lifted and the scar hidden in the bikini line. The ultrasonic body life additionally flattens the abdomen and smoothes the back.

Body lifting is a super-specialized area and results are dramatic for body fat and cellulite reduction. Complete information on this and all other procedures performed by Dr. Gilliland are available on his website: www.markgilliland.com

Despite a busy practice, Dr. Gilliland remains committed to academics: He is also a clinical assistant professor of plastic surgery at Baylor College of Medicine in Houston.

the beauty makers

the beauty makers
DR. HARRY MITTELMAN
900 Welch Road
Palo Alto, CA 94304
650-941-8888

Dr. Harry Mittelman

Dr. Harry Mittelman helped pioneer facial implant surgery, facial cosmetic laser surgery and techniques for facelift surgery.

The Mittelman Extended Chin Implants and the Mittelman Pre-Jowl Implants are used worldwide, and are among the most popular implants of that type used in the United States. In the mid nineteen eighties the doctor also pioneered the use of the Carbon Dioxide Laser for cosmetic surgery.

"When selecting a surgeon, it's important to choose one who has experience in the procedure you want performed," Dr. Mittelman said, "but it's equally important to know his or her philosophy of surgery and concepts of beauty.

"It's also important to individualize each consultation and surgical procedure, to listen to each patient's goals, desires and motivations, and to coordinate her or his objectives within the reality of what can be achieved safely. My goal is to always achieve the best aesthetic result within the context of safety and a natural, non-surgical look."

The Menlo Park, California-based physician has been practicing in the Palo Alto-Stanford area for more than twenty years, and said he and his colleague, Dr. Bradley Greene, are the only surgeons in the area who specialize exclusively in facial cosmetic surgery and body liposuction. He was among the first to perform body liposuction in Northern California, teaches on a national basis and is an associate clinical professor at Stanford University Medical Center.

"I can't stress enough the importance of being very selective in choosing the facial plastic surgeon and the team of professionals with whom you will be working to enhance your appearance," Dr. Mittelman said. "Over the years we've found that the patients who get the most improvement and who are most satisfied with the experience are patients who carefully select a surgeon and office support staff with whom they feel personally comfortable and at ease."

The doctor said it was of paramount importance for the patient to discuss general aesthetic and surgical philosophy with her or his surgeon as well as gathering information to learn about specific procedures.

"In our practice we strive to maximize facial symmetry and balance and, at the same time, achieve the most youthful and natural appearing face as possible," he said. "We avoid any procedures that may give an operated on, tight or plastic appearance.

"There are, obviously, risks, benefits and expectations that go along with all cosmetic plastic surgeries and procedures. Fortunately, with today's technology the extremely low level of risk in this specific surgical field is unprecedented. Conversely, the benefits of an expert facial plastic surgery and liposuction team have never been higher and in more demand than they are today. So we can provide to the patient the best cosmetic plastic surgery and aesthetic services available anywhere...in this country or abroad."

Procedures done by the Mittelman-Greene Plastic Surgery Center include facelift surgery, eyelid surgery, nose surgery, chin and cheek implants, liposculpture, turkey neck reduction, forehead and eyebrow lifting, laser skin resurfacing and chemical peels, Botox, collagen and dermalogen, lip augmentation, scar revision, ear set back, dermabrasion and microdermabrasion, laser removal of blood vessels and spider veins.

For skin rejuvenation the center uses a collagen-remodeling laser, which does not injure the superficial layer of skin during treatment.

"This laser uses a skin-cooling mechanism to protect the surface skin," Dr. Mittelman said.

For superficial exfoliative skin care and rejuvenation the center utilizes microdermabrasion, a process in which fine salt crystals are mechanically blown across the skin surface to remove dead skin cells and improve skin health and complexion.

Dr. Harry Mittelman

"This modality improves fine wrinkling, improves complexion and supplements a program of ongoing skin care maintenance and aging prevention," the doctor said.

Descriptions of all major procedures and information on what to expect during the post-operative or post-treatment period can be found on the center website: www.mittelmangreene.com. However, Dr. Mittelman said that while the descriptions are meant to be informative, they are not all-inclusive.

"The best way for an individual to learn about what procedures and treatments will give her or him the most improvement is to schedule an appointment with us for a facial analysis," he said. "Every individual requires a customized combination of surgical and non-surgical treatments to maximize her or his aesthetic improvement."

Dr. Mittelman said three principles guided (and continue to guide) the creation and maintenance of the operating facility and surgicenter in the Mittelman-Greene office-surgical complex – privacy, safety and quality.

"Our state-of-the-art, fully accredited surgicenter includes a waiting area and courtyard for family members and friends, a pre-operative holding area and a recovery area," he said. "The surgicenter is operated by a nursing staff and an MD anesthesiologist. It is devoted exclusively to facial plastic surgery and body liposuction. We believe this combination of location, facility and personnel maximizes the privacy, safety, comfort and overall quality of care of our patients."

A former major in the U.S. Air Force, Dr. Mittelman received his medical degree from, and did his residency at, the University of Kansas Medical Center. Certified by the American Board of Facial Plastic and Reconstructive Surgery and by the American Board of Cosmetic Surgery, he is a Fellow of the American Academy of Facial Plastic Surgery and the American Society of Liposuction Surgery.

Dr. Mittelman has been very active in the American Academy of Facial Plastic and Reconstructive Surgery. He was chosen by his peers to be on its board of directors and to serve as its treasurer for four years. He was also a founding member of the American Society for Laser Medicine and Surgery.

From the American Academy of Facial Plastic Surgery, in recognition for his contributions to the areas of facial contouring, rhinoplasty, laser as well as other areas of cosmetic surgery, he received the Mark Rafaty Award "for exceptional contributions to the field of plastic surgery." And he has also received the "Teacher of the Year" award at Stanford for his resident instruction and lectures about facial plastic surgery.

the beauty makers

the beauty makers
S. Maas, M.D.
Facial Plastic Surgery
DR. COREY S. MAAS
2400 Clay Street
San Francisco, CA 94143
(415) 567-7000

Dr. Corey S. Maas

Dr. Corey S. Maas specializes in facial plastic and reconstructive surgery, including minimally invasive office procedures with short recovery periods. His credentials include specialized training and experience in surgical procedures to reverse the signs of aging, refine facial features, correct congenital and acquired facial deformities and nasal disorders. Treatment outcomes reflect this level of training, experience and acknowledged expertise.

Dr. Maas is highly regarded as an expert in the area of aesthetic facial procedures and has been featured in numerous newspaper articles and television programs – and in popular women's magazines such as **Vogue** and **Allure**.

The San Francisco, California-based physician is director of the Appearance Care Center, which is affiliated with the University of San Francisco (UCSF) Medical Center – long considered one of the top medical and research centers in the world. The doctor combines his experience as an academic professor at the university with an active cosmetic and reconstructive surgery practice.

In addition to his surgical expertise, Dr. Maas brings to the Appearance Care Center an aesthetically oriented, patient focused approach that is unique. Consultation and facial analysis are individualized and provided in a comfortable office setting that provides computer assisted facial imaging. Ancillary consultations with nurse specialists, aestheticians and nutrition and fitness experts are appropriately used to treat each patient according to her or his individual needs.

"The Appearance Care Center offers care and service for patients with congenital and traumatic deformities of the face and neck in addition to cosmetic surgery of these areas," said Dr. Maas. "The goals for all such procedures are individualized for each patient to restore a balanced and youthful appearance without a superficial, operated look.

"We take great pride in our affiliation with the University of California's School of Medicine, an internationally renowned medical center and teaching institution. Our facilities are cutting edge, prompting the innovation in research and medical care that hallmark the UCSF Medical Center. But true excellence isn't about technology. It's about people. And our Center is recognized worldwide for its high standards...for the finest trained physicians, nurses and staff managing quality patient care."

The doctor said the Appearance Care Center include highly qualified physicians in the areas of dermatology and dermatologic surgery.

"These UCSF clinical faculty bring expertise in the management of surgical and non-surgical skin conditions such as aging, vascular (blood vessel) disorders, skin cancer, hair replacement, hair removal and body fat removal (liposuction)," he said.

"Our occuplastic surgeons (eyelid specialists) are expert in repairing complicated deformities of the eyelid and eyebrow area. These UCSF clinical professors also bring expertise in the facial area of lid sagging (ptosis), eyelid reconstruction and eyelid aging."

He said aesthetic nurse specialists on Appearance Care Center staff offer a number of ancillary treatments that include micro pigmentation (tattooing) of lips, eyebrows and skin color disorders; treatment of small facial vessels (sclerotherapy); facial peels and skin care regimens.

"Our aesthetic nurse specialists are highly trained and experienced, work under the close guidance of our physicians, and play an integral role in overall patient management," the doctor said.

The Appearance Care Center is affiliated with three different surgery centers in San Francisco. The UCSF Surgery Center is used for more intensive procedures and is fully accredited and staffed by UCSF specialists, anesthesiologists and physicians. This comprehensive facility is located at 400 Parnassus and maintains a full complement of state-of-the-art surgical equipment and support infrastructure.

Dr. Corey S. Maas

The California Pacific Medical Center (CPMC), located at 2333 Buchanan Street, recognized nationally for the excellence of its physicians and nurses, is employed for the provision of a variety of surgical services. And HealthSouth Surgery Center of San Francisco, located in Suite 200 at 1635 Divisadero, provides a variety of outpatient services and has earned a regional reputation as the "Center of Excellence for Outpatient Surgery."

"Facial scars, facial paralysis, facial and body fat, eyelids and forehead, wrinkles, folds and crows feet, ears, lips and smile lines, nose, chin and cheeks, face and neck and skin cancers...they're all among the plastic surgery procedures we correct," Dr. Maas said. "Our SoftForm procedure is a sub-dermal facial implant that is used to eliminate creases and furrows by providing structure and support underneath the skin. And we use Botulinum A Toxin (Botox) for the correction of wrinkles."

Dr. Maas received his medical education at the University of Florida College of Medicine, where he was an honors graduate. He continued his training with a surgical internship and residency at the St. Louis University School of Medicine and completed his specialty training with a fellowship in facial plastic and reconstructive surgery at the University of California San Francisco School of Medicine, where his achievements earned him an appointment to the full-time faculty.

He is board certified by the American Board of Facial Plastic and Reconstructive Surgery and the American Board of Otolaryngology – Head and Neck Surgery. He is also a Fellow of the American Academy of Facial Plastic and Reconstructive Surgery, the American Academy of Otolaryngology and the American College of Surgeons.

The doctor is an active member of numerous professional organizations and serves on the board of directors of the American Academy of Facial Plastic and Reconstructive Surgery. He is also a respected teacher and well-published researcher responsible for the surgical specialty education of medical students, residents and other clinicians.

Dr. Maas received the prestigious Sir Harold Delf Gilles Award from the American Academy of Facial Plastic and Reconstructive Surgery for groundbreaking research on surgical implant materials. He has also received numerous teaching accolades and, as an acknowledged authority in facial plastic surgery, is recruited as a lecturer by regional, national and international medical societies.

the beauty makers

the beauty makers
DR. H. GEORGE BRENNAN
1441 Avocado Avenue #707
Newport Beach, California 92660
(949) 644-1641

Dr. H. George Brennan

Dr. George Brennan says cosmetic surgery is the most unique field in medicine because it is the only "happy field."

The Newport Beach, California-based plastic surgeon was not being negative when he said the word "medicine" normally has a negative connotation. He was, rather, stating a fact.

"When a person becomes ill and goes to a doctor, it's with the hope that the doctor can help him or her get back to the degree of health he or she enjoyed before becoming sick," Dr. Brennan said. "The patient just wants to get back to what he or she perceives to be normal. But, truthfully, the patient is never actually better off when leaving a doctor's office or a hospital because of illness or injury than when they went in."

Cosmetic surgery, on the other hand, makes people happier and better, which is why Dr. Brennan said he chose the field as his specialty.

"When I was in medical school, I was being rotated to different areas of specialization to gain a spectrum of experience and perspective of each," he said. "When I rotated to facial plastic surgery where my brother was a resident, I was witness to a heroic procedure on a smoker who as a result had a hole in his throat and couldn't talk. Obviously, there wasn't much happiness on the part of the patient.

"But in a nearby cubicle there was a young girl who had received cosmetic surgery on her nose, and she was crying with joy.

"That was a clear message to me. I decided I wanted those types of patients instead of those like the smoker. There are ways to treat other addictions, but not smoking. I take my hat off to oncologists, but plastic surgery is more a fit for my psychological makeup."

Dr. Brennan said he was blessed to be in a field where surgery for a weak chin or bump on the nose provided a patient with predictably good results and no downside. He said that for the most part he dealt with people who wanted to improve their appearance, but who were not sick. But even in the "happy" art of cosmetic surgery, smokers cause problems.

"In the field of plastic surgery the problem patients are generally smokers," he said. "When you're dealing with a smoker who wants cosmetic surgery the red flags go up because the complication rate increases. That's not the case with a moderate drinker, but smoking and sun exposure are skin killers."

Dr. Brennan's commitment to early intervention and prevention led to the development of Newport Skin Care, a clinically proven prescription anti-aging formula that arrests sun damage and actually reverses it. He said the product even controls his twelve-year-old son's acne.

The doctor said the key to looking great without cosmetic surgery, of course, would be to pick your parents, but since that is not an option a person can help herself or himself with good nutritional habits, reasonable sun exposure, and by avoiding smoking, alcohol and recreational drugs.

Over the past thirty years there have been tremendous innovations in plastic surgery, Dr. Brennan said, and for the future he expects a continuing evolution of techniques and understanding of beauty.

"We are continually having to define beauty, what we can get with this patient and have her still be the same patient," he said. "After all, this is not reincarnation. So the surgeon and the patient have to become more and more understanding of beauty, and how it applies to the patient.

"One of the great things that has happened over the years is that cosmetic surgery is now socially acceptable. In the past it was sort of closet surgery for the elite and the rich, but it has evolved to the point where there is no stigma to it. In fact, people actually flaunt it."

Dr. Brennan said he was the first surgeon to develop the cheekbone implant, and that he also developed the "no hair loss" facelift –

no small matter since the downside of many facelifts is loss of a significant amount of hair.

"We promise no hair loss," he said, "because we have a hair preservation technique."

The doctor, who performs all surgeries himself, said that when a person was ready for a facelift could not be based on age, that a twenty-eight-year-old might need a lot of work whereas a fifty-year-old might not need any.

"The youngest person I know of to receive a facelift...not my patient...was a nine-year-old girl who had protruding ears," he said. "I did a facelift on a young ninety-year-old woman who goes dancing three nights a week. Rejuvenation is not age-related."

Dr. Brennan, owner of The Brennan Institute, with offices in Beverly Hills and Aspen, Colorado as well as Newport Beach, is author of the medical textbook, Aesthetic Facial Surgery. He is president-elect of the American Academy of Facial Plastic and Reconstructive Surgery, president of the Foundation for Facial Plastic Surgery, founder of the California Society for Cosmetic Surgery, frequent quest lecturer and instructor for national symposiums on aesthetic facial plastic surgery, and course director of an annual international symposium on "The Latest Advances in Cosmetic Surgery of the Face."

Triple board certified – American Board of Otolaryngology, American Board of Cosmetic Surgery and American Board of Facial Plastic and Reconstructive Surgery – he has been a contributing author to seven books and has been published in and submitted articles to numerous journals including **Advances in Otolaryngology Head and Neck Surgery**, **American Journal of Cosmetic Surgery**, **Annals of Plastic Surgery**, **Archives of Otolaryngology**, **EENT Monthly, International Surgery**, **Journal of Facial Plastic Surgery**, **Otolaryngology Digest**, and **Plastic and Reconstructive Surgery**.

A Michigan native, Dr. Brennan was educated at Wayne State University and the University of Michigan, did an internship at Santa Monica (California) Hospital and his residency at UCLA Medical Center and Wadswoth VA Hospital.

the beauty makers
DR. MICHAEL L. WALKER
206 West Windcrest
Fredericksburg, Texas 78624
830-997-0252

Dr. Michael L. Walker

here are a lot of reasons to travel to Fredericksburg, Texas for facial plastic surgery.

The first and foremost is Dr. Michael L. Walker, a world-class physician possessing the nation's highest facial plastic surgery credentials.

Second, a professional and qualified staff that is the equal of any in the world assists Dr. Walker.

Third, the Hill Country Facial Plastic Surgery Center is a Class C (highest achievable class) facility certified to the highest standards by the American Association for Accreditation of Ambulatory Surgical Facilities. The state-of-the-art surgery suite has been designed for comfort, convenience and privacy with all the safety features of a hospital location.

Fourth, there is no better place than the Hill Country to rejuvenate. Fredericksburg is an unforgettable small town west of Austin and San Antonio that has gained national prominence for its ambiance and unique shopping, restaurants, art galleries, antiques, historical museums and much more. Your brief recovery time spent in one of the town's serene "home away from home" bed and breakfast will refresh your spirit.

Dr. Walker has impeccable credentials. He is a Cum Laude graduate (BA) of the University of Texas in Austin, received his Doctor of Medicine (MD) degree from Baylor College of Medicine in Houston. He did an internship at Baylor Affiliated Hospitals, Texas Medical Center, in Houston and his residency at Eastern Virginia Medical Center/Naval Hospital, Portsmouth, Virginia.

He is board certified by the American Board of Facial Plastic and Reconstructive Surgery and the American Board of Otolaryngology/Head and Neck Surgery. He is also a Fellow of the

American Board of Facial Plastic and Reconstructive Surgery, American College of Surgeons, and the American Academy of Otolaryngology/Head and Neck Surgery.

Special distinctions include being a clinical instructor in otolaryngology/facial plastic surgery and the University of Texas Health Science Center in San Antonio and also being recipient of the Distinguished Education Award in Facial Plastic Surgery and the American Medical association Outstanding Physician Award in Continuing Medical Education.

He is a member of the Texas Medical Association, has served as president of the Hill County Medical Society and as chief of staff of Hill County Memorial Hospital.

While the aforementioned credentials are impressive, the doctor's years as a flight surgeon with the U.S. Navy gave him unparalleled opportunity to deal with a variety of battlefield wounds – facial fractures, facial trauma and head and neck wounds – that he says made him a better plastic surgeon.

"As chief of surgery of a naval hospital, I dealt with many severe cases that you might never experience in private practice," he said. "So those challenges make you a much better surgeon. That, at least, was my experience."

During his teen years the Houston native was not sure about a vocation, but did know that he wanted to fly. His mother was a PhD in education in the Memorial area of the city, so there was always an emphasis on education in the home. The desire to fly and emphasis on education led to his enrollment at the Marine Military Academy in Harlingen, Texas, which had an aerospace and ROTC program. He received his pilot license on his seventeenth birthday and commercial pilot license on his eighteenth birthday.

"I seriously considered going into the Marine Corps before going to college," Dr. Walker said, "but ended up going to the University of Texas where I studied psychology. That led to the premed program at the university."

When the doctor applied for admission to Baylor Medical

School in the seventies, there were four thousand applicants for one hundred sixty-eight positions.

"I was fortunate to be chosen," he said, "but some of the most memorable medical experience I received was as an orderly at Ben Taub Hospital while working on my pre-medical prerequisites."

The hospital to which Dr. Walker refers is the largest charity hospital in Houston, which has a reputation for being one of the best in the nation in dealing with trauma from gunshot and knife wounds, automobile and other types of accidents.

"You saw everything at Ben Taub," he said, "but something I'll never forget is a man with a knife buried in his forehead."

While at Baylor, Dr. Walker received a well-rounded education at the Texas Medical Center. There he had the good fortune to be trained by world-renowned surgeons Dr. Michael Debakey and Dr. Denton Cooley. Dr. Walker said he uses these two remarkable physicians as role models in being a caring, courteous gentleman surgeon and teacher.

The doctor joined the Navy soon after finishing his internship and was sent to flight school at Pensacola Naval Air Station as part of the Second Marine Air Wing. He spent some of his time in the Navy on the aircraft carrier Lexington.

He eventually ended up at the Naval Hospital in Corpus Christi, Texas, which is where he ended his fourteen-year Navy career prior to entering private practice. For six years he was director of surgery.

"Because of the endless supply of people in the military who needed facial plastic surgery, in two to three years I probably got ten years experience," he said. "There's a real art to plastic surgery. It requires discipline and attention to the smallest detail, which is why I enjoy doing it. And with rare exception a patient is always appreciative of what you have done."

As to why he chose the idyllic Fredericksburg setting for his practice, Dr. Walker said, "I decided that I wanted to raise my kids in a community where there was respect for the old values…and I haven't been disappointed.

"Many plastic surgeons think they have to be in a major city to attract patients, but we have patients coming to us from all over the globe. A lot of people simply don't want to have their surgery done in the city where they live, but even more people following surgery prefer to refresh their spirit in a place like Fredericksburg."

Dr. Walker and his wife, Mary Ann, a registered operating room nurse, are joined together as a family team to care for their cosmetic surgery guests. Mary Ann is an aesthetic consultant who, with fifteen years of plastic surgery experience, interviews patients, discusses their concerns and suggests possible solutions that her husband can provide. The doctor said most guests are more relaxed discussing their problems with a knowledgeable cosmetic surgery nurse prior to focusing on the technical questions they later ask him when he interviews them.

If a patient decides to schedule surgery, he or she becomes one of the cosmetic practice's family guests, because Dr. Walker and his wife are a family team providing a personalized plan for each guest. Many guests are from out-of-town so bed and breakfast arrangements can be made with all meal services, if necessary, for the days of recuperation.

Fredericksburg is a well-known destination resort with more than three hundred and fifty bed and breakfast accommodations, along with art galleries and antique shops. There are, the doctor said, a multitude of diversions to entertain visitors who might decide on an extended stay.

House calls are arranged to check on post-operative guests and to make sure they are comfortable and care for during their convalescence.

The doctor said that in choosing a cosmetic surgeon, a person should select a physician that is doing the desired procedure on a regular basis.

"The surgeon must perform the procedures you are interested in on a regular basis to keep his or her skills up to date," he said.

Dr. Michael L. Walker

"Some cosmetic surgeons specialize in treating the face, while others perform procedures on all parts of the body. This makes a big difference in how many face lifts or eye lifts a surgeon performs in a given week or month.

"Also, board certification means the surgeon has undergone the rigorous training necessary to be qualified.

"Viewing before and after photos of the surgeon's former patients is equally important. Pay attention to the scars as well as the results. And make sure you feel comfortable asking questions of the surgeon and that your concerns are heard."

the beauty makers
DR. DEVINDER MANGAT
133 Barnwood Dr.
Edgewood, KY 41017
859-331-9600

Dr. Devinder Mangat

"I can't put a smile on their face with surgery," Dr. Mangat, the nationally respected facial plastic surgeon, said of his patients "But the resulting infusion of confidence can. I get a lot of satisfaction seeing the patient afterward, getting to see the smile on their face that wasn't there before."

Those smiles repay Dr. Mangat for all of the years of preparation, surgical training and personal sacrifice that he has experienced.

One of Dr. Mangat's most rewarding cases was that of a seventeen-year-old girl from the Ukraine. The girl was born with a birth defect that occupied almost half of her face. She had been treated previously with radiation treatments, but the Soviets, at that time, could not offer reconstructive plastic surgery. The x-ray treatments left her with a horrible scar about which she was painfully self-conscious. Because of her appearance, her self-esteem was very low.

"She had no self-image; she looked sad and acted sad," said Dr. Mangat.

When Dr. Mangat heard of her case, he agreed to do the surgery and he convinced a local hospital to provide the facilities and services for the surgeries.

Since the girl happened to live in Kharkiv, the Ukrainian Sister City to Cincinnati, Ohio, the Soviet government allowed her to travel to Cincinnati to receive reconstructive facial plastic surgery.

"I did a multi-stage reconstruction of the girl's face," said Dr. Mangat. "I didn't completely eliminate the scarring, but succeeded in improving her appearance quite dramatically."

It took about four years to reconstruct the girl's face. But for both the girl and Dr. Mangat, it was worth the time and effort.

"After the reconstruction, her appearance was changed to the extent that it gave her a completely new outlook on life," Dr. Mangat said.

The girl became confident and decided, with the zeal that comes from getting a fresh start, to do something meaningful with her life. After the breakup of the Soviet Union, the girl moved to Canada and pursued a master's in social work.

"Her plan is to help children," said Dr. Mangat.

With a similar zeal, Dr. Mangat left his own home country to come to the United States to learn medicine.

A native of Kenya, Dr. Mangat was raised by Indian parents who moved to Kenya in the days when it was still a British colony. When he finished secondary school in Nairobi, he decided he wanted to go to the United States for college. Being one of five children, Dr. Mangat knew he would first have to convince his parents to allow him to study in the United States. He promised his father that if he would pay for one year of education in the States, he would do well enough scholastically to get a scholarship for the remainder of his college education.

He selected Texas A&M because it was the southernmost university that he was interested in attending. "I wanted to go to school in a place with the warmest climate possible so that I would not be too homesick for Kenya," he said.

After a year at Texas A&M, Mangat kept his promise to his father. He transferred to the University of Kentucky, where he was granted a tuition scholarship that he maintained throughout his undergraduate and medical school. After medical school, he interned at the University of Iowa. Following his internship, he received a year of general surgery training back at the University of Kentucky and head-and-neck surgery at the University of Oklahoma.

During his head-and-neck surgery residency, he realized that he enjoyed highly detailed and meticulous work. His professors noticed this and encouraged him to make facial plastic surgery his subspecialty. As a result, Mangat was offered a fellowship in facial plastic surgery at the McCullough Facial Surgery Clinic in Birmingham,

Alabama under the auspices of the American Academy of Facial Plastic and Reconstructive Surgery.

"When planning a facial plastic surgical procedure, one has to think three-dimensionally," he said. "Plastic surgery is similar to soft sculpture. In addition to having superior technical skills, you also have to possess an aesthetic sense to do it. As a Facial Plastic Surgeon, I have to constantly be aware of "the look" that is considered attractive because, historically, that has changed from decade to decade. It is important to create that attractive, yet natural appearance in my patients.

"When I was training, I worked diligently at learning as much as I could about as many facets of facial plastic surgery as possible," explained Dr. Mangat. "I knew this would be key to becoming a confident and fully competent facial plastic surgeon whom patients would be able to trust whenever they required help – and be completely happy about coming to."

In facial plastic surgery, Mangat believes that he helps to make a difference in the lives of his patients with his meticulous nature and personal attention.

"My staff is trained to make every patient feel welcome. When patients make the first contact with our office, we talk to them on the phone about their interest and send them information in the mail about procedures that are relevant to them," said Dr. Mangat. "If they decide they want a consultation, they come into the office and we interview each other... I ask the patient questions about them and they ask questions about me. It is a time where we get to know each other. We have long-term relationships with our patients and we want to know who they are and they want to know us before we plan any surgical procedures. If we feel comfortable with each other, then we begin the process of facial analysis and a thorough examination that allows me to make the best recommendations for the patient's needs.

"We discuss the patient's desired result and together talk about what kind of procedures can achieve the results they want. Using my expertise, I make recommendations based on what I see. My guideline for recommendations is 'If that person were a family member, what would I recommend to them?'

"During the entire process, I try to be very conscious about the patient's confidence in me and in the procedures that we discuss. There's always something missing if the patient does not have confidence; without which the individual may not be happy no matter how great the surgical result.

"Several days after the consultation, a member of my staff contacts that patient to find out if they have any other questions. The staff member calling the patient is well versed in procedures and can answer additional questions. More importantly, the patient knows someone personally on my staff who they can call during the entire surgical experience."

Although his practice keeps him very busy, Dr. Mangat stays very active in his personal life. "I hate sitting still," he said. "I'm very goal-oriented and like to do athletic or constructive things." Dr. Mangat loves the outdoors and is a serious runner, road cyclist, skier and climber. He is also a wine connoisseur and loves to travel. But most of all, he loves to spend time with his children. "The biggest pleasure for me in life is the respect and love of my children," said Dr. Mangat.

Dr. Mangat performs almost all of his procedures at his accredited surgery center in Edgewood, Kentucky, where he has three operating rooms and four recovery rooms. He also has a second office in Cincinnati and third in Vail, Colorado. He's in Vail about once a month for four or five days at a time and does some surgery at the local hospital. The three locations provide a diverse patient clientele, which includes a number of celebrities.

But plastic surgery is not just for celebrities. Dr. Mangat still gets letters and visits from the Ukrainian girl who never fails to mention how he changed her life. And that makes Dr. Mangat smile.

the beauty makers

the beauty makers
DR. E. FRED AGUILAR
6410 Fannin #927
Houston, Texas 77030
(713) 797-0085

Dr. E. Fred Aguilar

Dr. E. Fred Aguilar is not only one of the country's premiere plastic and reconstructive surgeons, he is also an innovator who does groundbreaking surgery for children born without ears.

"Ear surgery on children is very satisfying," he said, "because it enables these kids to go out in public with much better self-esteem. They feel they have a better handle on life."

The Houston, Texas doctor, who has performed ear surgery on hundreds of children since nineteen eighty-six, said creating ears on children who were born without one or both ears requires consummate skill and art in plastic surgery.

"Sculpting rib cartilage into an ear requires a good three-dimensional eye," he said. "And the artistic ability to deliver that takes ongoing practice and maturity. This kind of ear surgery is painstaking and time-consuming. A child must undergo a series of four to five operations, depending on whether he or she is a candidate for having the hearing restored. Most don't have an ear canal or an eardrum."

Dr. Aguilar's specialties are rhinoplasty (nose surgery), breast augmentation, liposuction, facelifts and ear surgery.

"My training is different from that of some plastic surgeons," he said. "I spent nine years doing facial plastic surgery and learning all the nuances that are important for correcting the aging face, all within the mantra of facial plastic surgery. After years of success in facial plastic surgery, I had so many patients who wanted procedures for other parts of their bodies that I found it incumbent to go back into the field of plastic surgery to obtain the extra credentials to excel in these multiple disciplines."

The doctor said memories of satisfied patients and their testimonials are constant reminders of why he chose to become a plastic surgeon.

"It's very satisfying to have a face lift patient tell me I've helped turn her life around, and improve her social calendar, or to help a young girl who had a hump on her nose become more extroverted and less self-conscious when she sees a guy looking at her at a stop-light, " he said. " And there's nothing that can compare with the smile of a child who looks in the mirror and sees an ear where he or she didn't have one before, or to see a breast augmentation patient who is proud to be a woman and who now has renewed confidence and self-esteem."

Dr. Aguilar said his commitment to detail and patient satisfaction, along with the caring and information he dispenses, is what makes his practice unique.

"Although there are no guarantees in medicine, my commitment to my patients lasts for a year after surgery -- to ensure that they are as happy as they can be with the results."

The doctor said he loves the fact that plastic surgery enables him to be artistic, while at the same time allowing him to remain within the field of medicine.

"Plastic surgery, specifically, provides an environment that brings new surprises every day and gives me a way to apply artistic concepts to different patients' forms," he said. "But, unfortunately, there are many myths and misconceptions about cosmetic surgery."

"Some people actually think they can choose any plastic surgeon and that their results will turn out fine. That's simply not true. Also, some people who want a procedure will get on the Internet and ask doctors to submit low bids. But it's important to remember that not all physicians who do cosmetic surgery are plastic surgeons."

Dr. Aguilar said there are gynecologists, dermatologists and even family practice doctors doing plastic surgery.

"It's legal," he said, "but you have to ask yourself if it's your best choice. So when you're interviewing doctors be sure to ask whether he or she is a plastic surgeon who is board certified or board eligible by the American Board of Plastic Surgery. And also remember that all plastic surgeons are not equally talented. Just like lawyers, teachers and plumbers, some are good and some aren't."

The doctor further warns that a patient should not consider his or her surgery finished when they leave the operating room.

"Patients should be made to understand that it takes time for swelling to recede," he said. "For example, when I remove the splint from a patient's nose after surgery, he or she won't see the final result. An improvement will be seen, but it takes weeks and sometimes months for the swelling to subside."

In about six months, Dr. Aguilar said, the nose will "settle" in and the patient will see the final result.

"Some people think the surgery is over the day they have it," he said, "which is what I call the McDonald's Syndrome. They can buy a burger at McDonald's, get it quickly and satisfy their hunger. But plastic surgery is not about instant gratification. I always warn patients to expect swelling, and try to get them to understand that their final look is weeks down the road."

Another myth, the doctor said, is that plastic surgeons can work miracles.

"The patient must have realistic expectations," he said. "We can make small steps that improve appearance, but we can't turn every woman into a glamour queen or every man into a handsome marquee idol. That's unrealistic."

Dr. Aguilar said many people think a good plastic surgeon will not leave scars.

"There will be scars," he said. "We make them as small and hidden as possible, but there are scars. If a doctor is honest, he or she will not mislead you about that."

"I want everyone who chooses me as their plastic surgeon to have a good experience, and I'll do everything within my power to make that happen. If I tell a patient I'm worried, he or she can believe it. If I say I'm not, they can believe that, too. Rapport between the patient and plastic surgeon is critical, so when a person decides to have surgery with me they are well educated regarding the procedure."

Born in St. Louis, Missouri, Dr. Aguilar earned his undergraduate degree at the University of Texas in El Paso and his MD from Texas Tech University School of Medicine in Lubbock. He did residencies at the University of Texas Medical School at Houston in plastic and reconstructive surgery, otolaryngology (head and neck surgery), and general surgery.

He is certified by the American Board of Plastic Surgery, American Board of Otolaryngology, and the American Board of Facial Plastic surgery.

Academic appointments include Clinical Assistant Professor in the Division of Plastic Surgery and the Department of Otolaryngology at the University of Texas Health Science Center, and the Division of Plastic Surgery at Baylor College of Medicine.

the beauty makers

the beauty makers
DR. HARRISON LEE
9001 Wilshire Boulevard #305
Beverly Hills, California 90211
(310) 777-2627

Dr. Harrison Lee

Prospective patients most often view plastic surgery simply as a procedure to beautify or enhance their appearance, to correct deformities, or to diminish signs of aging. Some believe erroneously that undergoing plastic surgery will change them into a new person or eliminate emotional scars they may have suffered over their appearance. Dr. Harrison Lee holds a clearer view of the craft and strives to educate his patients in adopting his approach.

"I think physical beauty is just appearing natural and that enhancing a patient's beauty to a natural state is of prime importance," he explains. "Undergoing plastic surgery simply to change ones appearance or become a different person is an illusion that often brings unfavorable results. I try to instill that view in all of my patients before proceeding with any surgical procedure."

Dr. Lee's approach is to assist nature rather than radically change it.

"I don't rush patients into making a decision," he says. "I want them to fully understand what they are undergoing and clearly know what results to expect. Even though it may just be cosmetic surgery, they have to take it seriously. Plastic surgery is individualized and is a very personal thing. I want my patients to understand that, so I spend as much time with them as possible, explaining the procedure and always encouraging a second consultation. If everything I say doesn't sink in during a first visit or if the surgery is extensive and complicated, I automatically schedule the second consultation. It is far better to know where a procedure will lead then to fly on the wings of illusion."

Dr. Lee speaks with authority, having earned his undergraduate degree in nineteen eighty from Tufts University and his dental degree from Tufts University School of Dental Medicine in nineteen eighty-three. He then went on to complete a residency in oral and maxillo-facial surgery. To further his knowledge, he also earned a medical degree from New York Medical College in nineteen ninety-two and served a residency in Otolaryngology-Head and Neck Surgery at New York's prestigious Mount Sinai Medical Center. He continued his quest for knowledge by pursuing a fellowship in facial plastic and reconstructive surgery in Beverly Hills, California.

Dr. Lee then founded the Center for Maxillo-Facial Plastic Surgery in Beverly Hills. Prospective patients can approach him with full confidence in his professionalism. He is board certified by the American Board of Facial Plastic and Reconstructive Surgery, the American Board of Otolaryngology-Head and Neck Surgery, and the American Board of Oral and Maxillo-Facial Surgery. He also serves as Clinical Assistant Professor at the University of Southern California School of Medicine.

Dr. Lee is a Fellow of the American College of Surgeons and a member of numerous medical societies. He has delivered a number of national and international presentations and is widely published in his field. He has earned the respect of many elite medical practitioners. His unique background in both medicine and dentistry, has given him a deep appreciation for the facial form and he is committed to a surgical practice that thrives on the cutting edge of medicine.

Dr. Lee comes from a family of medical experts and was destined early in life to pursue the profession. "My parents are all doctors," he says. "My dad is a general surgeon. He was a big influence in my life. My mother is a retired OBGYN and my two grandparents were OBGYNs. My great grandfather attended the University of Louisville, Kentucky in nineteen three, then went back to Korea and became dean of one of the leading medical schools. I was something of a black sheep. I wanted to do something different, so I became a dentist, practicing oral and maxillo-facial surgery. Yet, I somehow knew that I, too, would settle more solidly in medicine. So I changed direction and followed in my family's footsteps."

Dr. Harrison Lee

Dr. Lee doesn't restrict his treatment to the surgical theatre. "I try to impress on my patients the fact that surgery is not the only way to gain a favorable appearance," he says. "They can often maintain their appearance through a sensible diet and plenty of exercise. I also stress a positive outlook on life as a means good health. I don't like to recommend surgery when these other alternatives exist. I just don't want to go in there and cut, collect my fee and send my patients on their way. I want to treat them as I would want to be treated...with dignity and respect."

The doctor says, "I was born in Seoul, Korea, and came to this country in nineteen sixty-three when I was five years old, so I'm at home in the American culture. For fun I dabble in martial arts. When people get to know me they find me quiet and subdued on the outside, but inside I'm more energetic. I may not always express myself a whole lot, yet I do care and have a lot of compassion for everyone. People seem to learn that after knowing me for quite a while."

Dr. Harrison Lee is a family man and addresses family life as his prime interest outside of his work environment. "My fulfillment is my family and my kids," he says.

Dr. Lee calls himself a Zen Christian and believes that everyone should better observe and practice good fellowship. He has little time for community involvement or special hobbies.

"All I do is work," he explains. "My practice is my life. I enjoy being a doctor and caring not only for, but also about, my patients. My greatest joy is when they show their appreciation for my services or call me to see how I am doing. I'm thankful for my gifts. I think my great talent is my hands and that I was born with dexterity. For me, there is nothing more fulfilling than to use one's gifts in helping others."

the beauty makers

DR. JULIO GALLO, M.D.
16800 NW 2nd Avenue #607
N. Miami Beach, Florida 33169
(305) 651-9903

Dr. R. Julio Gallo

Great professionals are often a product of challenging circumstances. Like fine metal they become shaped and hardened through the fires of adversity and self-sacrifice.

Dr. Julio Francesco Gallo found his profession through such a transformation.

He was born in Hollywood, Florida, of immigrant parents. His father was an Italian who migrated to Cuba after World War Two. There, he met and married Dr. Gallo's mother, a Cuban national. Dr. Gallo's older brother was born there but after the revolution in nineteen sixty the family was exiled from the newly formed communist nation. His first job was that of assistant to his father who labored as a sculptor in a small art studio. To earn extra money, Dr. Gallo's father taught art classes at night. His exposure to his father's skills made an early impression. He developed a love for working with his hands that was to lead him ultimately to a successful career in plastic surgery.

Dr. Gallo's parents inspired him to work hard and be persistent in his endeavors. "They were major influences in my life," he says. "They had to restart their lives twice over because of political turmoil. Their perseverance and positive attitude has given me a different outlook on life. We make our own successes."

The doctor's brother was another influence. It was his interest in science that lured Dr. Gallo to similar pursuits. "I believe I pursued a career in medicine because my older brother went into medicine. He became a neurologist," Dr. Gallo says. "When we were growing up we both had a fascination with science and I recall many experiments we conducted on a daily basis. In high school and undergraduate studies, I pursued these interests in the sciences further. However, because of my father, I retained a certain love of art and the humanities. Combining them both in facial plastics was ideal for me. The three dimensional nature of the face, the analysis required, and the technical aspects of surgery all combined to thrill me."

While in medical school, Gallo found yet another mentor. "Dr. Robert L. Simmons taught me not only the technical aspects of surgery, but also the more human aspects of patient care, professionalism, and ethical medical behavior. I benefited greatly from his counsel and instruction."

Dr. Gallo's school years were filled with honors. From nineteen seventy-seven to nineteen eighty-one, he attended Chaminade College Preparatory School in Hollywood, Florida. While there, he was chosen valedictorian, became a member of the National Honor Society, attained First Honors, and made the Dean's List. In nineteen seventy-nine, he received a National Merit Scholarship Program Letter of Commendation and, in nineteen eighty, won the Rensselaer Polytechnic Institute Award for Math and Sciences.

In nineteen eighty-five, Dr. Gallo graduated Summa Cum Laude from the University of Miami at Coral Gables, Florida, earning a B.S. in biology/religion with departmental honors in biology.

From nineteen eighty-five until nineteen eighty-nine, Dr. Gallo attended the University of Chicago-Pritzker School of Medicine where he earned his M.D. Afterward, he served his internship in general surgery at Jackson Memorial Hospital/ University of Miami. He then fulfilled residency requirements, specializing in Otolaryngology-Head and Neck Surgery.

In nineteen ninety-four he became a Fellow, Facial Plastic and Reconstructive Surgery at Robert L. Simmons, M.D./ University of Miami, and in nineteen ninety-five was board certified in head and neck surgery via the American Board of Otolaryngology. In two thousand, he became a Fellow of the American College of Surgeons.

Dr. Julio Francesco Gallo maintains a practice today with fellow surgeons at the Simons Center for Nasal and Facial Plastic Surgery in North Dade County, Florida. Dr. Simons is an internationally recognized authority on facial plastic and reconstructive surgery. The center is known for its personal approach to helping patients achieve a natural look in the care of highly skilled, board-certified surgeons. Dr. Gallo and his associates are dedicated to providing patients with the latest medical advances that make it possible to improve the appearance and restore the function of features marred by age, disease, accident, or heredity.

Highly respected by his peers, Dr. Gallo has published many articles in medical journals and frequently presents lectures at medical symposiums. His training included experience with laser techniques, endoscopic facial plastic surgery, and other minimally invasive procedures. He is trained in laser surgery for the elimination of wrinkles and vascular blemishes, as well as scar removal. He also has extensive experience in reconstructing defects left after the removal of skin cancers.

Dr. Gallo has a strong relationship with his patients. "We are partners in the surgical procedure and the healing process," he explains. "I consider the patient equally important in the decision making process. I like to communicate with my patients. It is important for them to be as candid as possible with me and I will do the same. We must be able to reach a level of understanding so that we can proceed appropriately. I can give my advice, experience and judgment but we both have to agree as to a plan of action. A patient's happiness and satisfaction measures my success."

Dr. Gallo also believes that his patients must do their homework before undertaking treatment. "The best advice I can give is to become informed," he says. "The more patients know about procedures and postoperative care the better the chances for success. This requires research that can be accomplished by surfing the web, reading authoritative books about it (not necessarily popular magazines), and most importantly by talking to friends and relatives who have undergone facial plastic procedures and can give first-hand advice. I encourage all who are considering plastic surgery to become well informed. My most difficult cases often involve patients who are uninformed and have gathered unrealistic expectations."

Dr. Gallo also recommends effective preventive maintenance.

"Eat well, exercise and avoid toxins...this means smoking, sun, and so on," he says. "A good skin care regimen at home and regular facials also help to maintain a fresh appearance."

Dr. Gallo, the man, is as dedicated as Dr. Gallo, the surgeon. He loves to exercise. "I feel it is really important to be in touch with one's own body," he says. "I ran the New York Marathon twice. Completing that was a great achievement for me. I feel that balance is critical between body and mind. I enjoy the movies, opera, theater and reading. I also love to travel and discover new places and, most importantly, new people and cultures. By understanding others, I think we become more in touch with ourselves as humans and as a society."

The doctor's outlook on life compliments his professional status. His key interest is in caring for his patients and others. "I learned the value of caring at a turning point in my life," he explains. "When my father developed a brain tumor, I had to take care of him until he passed away. He died in his most productive years when he was doing the most interesting sculptural works. That experience gave me a different view of patient care. It gave me a different outlook on life. I realized what a short time we have here and how we must learn to spend that time well."

Dr. Gallo displays that attitude toward time well spent far beyond the boundaries of his practice. He is actively involved in the arts. "I was the chair of the board of trustees for a local arts center that has expanded significantly during my tenure of the last four years," he says. "This is particularly important to me because it was an art center my father helped establish more than thirty years ago when he first arrived in this country."

He also serves as a voluntary clinical instructor at the University of Miami/ Jackson Memorial Hospital where he is involved in teaching facial plastic surgery to residents. In addition, Dr. Gallo serves on the board of the Primo Camera Society, raising funds for underprivileged children. His trip from the crucible of his beginnings has been filled with great accomplishments, not just for himself, but also for legions of others.

the beauty makers

the beauty makers
DR. FRANCIS PALMER
8500 Wilshire Boulevard #900
Beverly Hills, California 90211
(310) 652-9583

Dr. Francis Palmer

Doctor Francis Palmer holds an aesthetic view of plastic surgery.

"It is probably one of the last remaining examples of hand-made craftsmanship," he relates.

Palmer believes in artistic craftsmanship, individualized treatment, and much more.

"I believe that a truly gifted plastic surgeon must have the eyes of an artist, the hands of an angel, and the heart of a lion," Palmer asserts. "This enables one to decide what will make the patient more attractive while gently and deftly shifting tissues with the utmost courage and skill, as the surgeon quite literally holds the outward identity of his/her patient in his/her hands.... A tremendous responsibility that must not be taken lightly."

Palmer's original career path was not in the direction of medicine. Business was his first choice. His first job was as a printer's assistant and later he worked as a landscaper and house painter. His house painting skills helped him through college where he sought a business degree with a major in marketing.

"I had to put myself through undergraduate school so actually started my own painting contracting business that I ran for five or six years. To do that I had to develop all the business plans, books, the accounting, the advertising, and so forth. My business classes were somewhat boring because I was already accomplished in running my own enterprise. Yet, I had to do that to survive," Palmer explains.

Palmer's college studies also included a number of required science courses that soon came to intrigue him.

"Science was extremely challenging and the more courses I took the more I enjoyed them", he explains. "I was a senior in marketing when I actually switched over and decided to take pre-med. I entered San Diego State University and did some externship in their large student health program. I was under the instruction of a retired general surgeon who was in charge of the program. I followed him around for a year and a half assisting in various procedures. The surgeon was a mentor. He stimulated my interest and further influenced my decision to go into medicine."

Graduating with honors, Palmer then entered the University of California Irvine School of Medicine where he received his M.D. degree. He then served a five-year residency in Head and Neck Surgery at USC-LA County Medical Center (the largest medical teaching institution in the world). During his tenure major emphasis was placed on facial plastic surgery.

Following board certification, Dr. Palmer completed a one-year fellowship with the American Academy of Facial Plastic and Reconstructive Surgery, and was board certified with the American Board of Facial Plastic and Reconstructive Surgery. He later completed a one-year fellowship in Cosmetic Surgery of the Face and Body with the American Academy of Cosmetic Surgery and is board eligible with the American Board of Cosmetic Surgery.

Dr. Palmer has been Director of Facial Plastic Surgery for the Head and Neck Surgery Department at the University of Southern California School of Medicine since nineteen ninety-one, and was recently named "One Of The World's Best" Aesthetic Plastic Surgeons by the international media.

Although born and raised in Pennsylvania, Palmer makes his home and directs his practice in California. His Los Angeles based Beverly Hills International Center for Aesthetic Surgery, describes by title alone, Dr. Palmer's approach to his craft.

"We strive to offer the most up-to-date plastic surgery procedures in a state-of-the art surgical facility," Palmer explains. "Ours is a fully accredited, licensed outpatient surgery center where through a combination of surgical mastery, artistic vision, and sound aesthetic judgment I strive to meet my patients' expectations."

Dr. Palmer defines plastic surgery as the art of aesthetically enhancing the human physical form. When properly performed, according to Palmer, it can dramatically improve one's appearance in restoring the natural beauty of youth.

"Its results should be natural, attractive and enhancing," he asserts.

Palmer hopes that potential patients will know what they want to achieve. If they aren't sure of their needs, Palmer tries to assist.

"A surgeon who is truly gifted will be able to sit down with a patient and tell them what will make them look more attractive and what won't. That's what I try to relay to each patient," he explains.

Dr. Palmer doesn't ignore his responsibility to educate his patients. Preventive maintenance is his key advice. "If you buy a new car, you learn to take care of it, giving it regular maintenance so that it will deliver top performance over a long term. The same is true of our bodies and our skin in particular. You don't ignore symptoms and wait until parts start falling off your car, neither should you ignore poor skin conditions and wait until they need serious treatment."

Palmer recommends typical good maintenance techniques, including sun exposure avoidance, a healthy diet, weight control, ample consumption of liquids, and exercise. He also explains that beauty maintenance is important and that everyone needs to commit to it. "Your degree of maintenance will depend on your social situation and how you feel. Facials and non-invasive skin treatments may help rejuvenate your skin without surgery." Most important to remember is that you don't have to let everything fall apart before you seek help or consultation," Palmer cautions.

Dr. Palmer is a renowned plastic surgeon who has earned worldwide praise through his surgeries and teaching programs. Unlike many surgeons, Palmer performs all of the surgery himself, including the final suturing...something other top surgeons relegate to assistants or nurses. Palmer feels it is worth the extra time, and money, for the patient to have him close the incision. Palmer takes his practice very seriously.

"I consider it to be the 'Rolls Royce' of practices," he explains, "where every person's beauty potential is seen as unique and deserving of the highest quality surgery with the highest level of comfort, compassion and confidentiality."

Dr. Palmer's patients, peers, and students share his pursuit of perfection, and have showered him with praise. **Goodlife Magazine** called him an "Internationally renowned facial Plastic Surgeon – who not only puts shape back in a woman's face by subtly sculpting the facial skeletal structure, he also creates a beautiful neck, for so long a standard of feminine beauty – One of the leading American Plastic Surgeons."

Miami Weekly heralded Palmer as a "famous surgeon – Performing miracles – The skilled hands of this surgeon have reshaped some of the most famous faces of our time – a modern day sculptor would best describe this surgeons talents – His innovative and cutting edge procedures have been documented in countless journals – the pride this man exudes when speaking about his work leaves you confident and optimistic about your decision to have plastic surgery."

Tatler Magazine also heaped kudos on Palmer and his work. "You simply can't afford to make a mistake with cosmetic surgery, so get the best – Palmer is the surgeon to many famous faces – Discretion is everything, but look in the pages of any society and film magazine and you'll be unwittingly admiring his work – he has pioneered new techniques in facial cosmetic surgery."

Woman's World Magazine called Palmer "a renowned Hollywood Plastic Surgeon – with his specialized beauty boosts – you can look movie-star famous."

London's Daily Express praised Palmer for making "subtlety his byword – his facial contour facelift is the nearest thing to a miracle."

"Plastic surgery is true artistry", says Dr. Palmer, who is authoring an upcoming book revealing his revolutionary new concepts of beauty and aesthetics in plastic surgery.

"Plastic surgery, in order to be inspired work, must incorporate both the art and science of beauty. The surgeon must have an aesthetic eye."

This philosophy has led to the development of two of Dr. Palmer's trademarked techniques that are helping shape the future of plastic surgery: the "Facial Contour®" Facelift and the "Ever Full®" Lip Enhancement. Males and females both become more masculine appearing as they age. Palmer's procedures artistically bring out facial features, thereby giving the face a more contoured youthful anatomy. This information and much more is presented on Dr. Palmer's web site at http://www.beverlyhills-plasticsurgery.com.

"There is a great reward I find in practicing my craft," Palmer says. "Seeing the results through the eyes of the patient or the patient's loved ones can be very moving. I recall a difficult surgery to reduce the large nose of a very attractive teenage girl. When the cast came off her family and friends who were present began to weep. Their weeping was for joy as one of them said, 'Oh my God, honey, now you are pretty again.' Those simple words were very powerful and they brought home to me how vital, challenging, and fulfilling my work can be."

Francis Palmer isn't just a highly accomplished surgeon. He is a well-rounded individual whose hobbies include tennis, skiing, and roaming the beach. He is also an artist, who for relaxation, paints in watercolor, oil, and acrylic mediums rendering a style he likes to describe as photo-realism.

Palmer too, is a devout Christian and dedicated family man, who while enjoying the fulfillment of his profession finds his greatest pleasure in being a husband and father.

"The most satisfaction in my life is my family. They come first," Palmer insists. "My practice fulfills a large part of my life and gives me great pleasure in being able to make people more attractive. But at the end of the day I go home to simple hugs from my wife, son, and daughter...that gives my life true meaning."

the beauty makers
GARTH FISHER, M.D., F.A.C.S.
120 South Spalding Drive – Suite 222
Beverly Hills, California 90212
(310) 273-5995

Dr. Garth Fisher

hirty years ago she was a top fashion model gracing the covers of Vogue and Harpers Bazaar. The desire to regain a measure of that bygone aesthetic beauty, that time when her sense of her self-esteem had been enhanced by her classic allure, held her captive.

The mission was clear.

She sought the care of one of the most respected plastic cosmetic surgeons in the country. Her anticipated surgical transformation was thought to be so dramatic that NBC's Today Show made a decision. The transformation was to be captured on film. Thus, millions of viewers took part in the unveiling during one week in November 2002, when the Today Show aired five consecutive segments documenting her facelift and subsequent healing process, culminating with an appearance by both the former super model and her surgeon on national television.

The show: Forever Young.

Three candidates from across America were chosen from thousands of applicants to undergo a cosmetic surgical transformation, completely changing their appearance and their lives. The entire process was captured on film and broadcast on ABC's new reality television show in December 2002 – The Extreme Makeover.

Skyrocketing ratings caused ABC to air the show again one week later. So successful were those ratings that ABC contracted with the show's producer to schedule a series of six additional episodes.

So there were two nationally televised "makeovers" on two competing national networks within one month, but just one plastic surgeon, chosen from hundreds – unprecedented in an era of competing networks.

The plastic surgery capital of the world is located ten miles east of the Pacific Ocean, where luxury and excitement intersect on a swollen corridor known as much for its fancy boutiques as for the private reservation telephone numbers of its maitre d's.

Here in Beverly Hills the rich and the famous gather to shop, eat and be seen, but even more important to look great and feel pampered. In the field of plastic surgery, only the most successful survive.

Here in the most famous real estate triangle in the United States there is one plastic surgeon that doesn't advertise. His reputation speaks for itself. His name is whispered at cocktail parties and in dressing rooms at the most prestigious boutiques in the country, from Madison Avenue to Rodeo Drive.

In Los Angeles a gifted plastic surgeon commands center stage, no less so than when an Oscar winning director accepts an award at the Kodak Theater. That's because in LA youth and beauty are venerated above all else; everyone is a star, or wants to look like one.

Dr. Garth Fisher, who led what ABC's The Extreme Makeover producers termed the "dream team" of professionals, is one of the most sought after and respected plastic surgeons in the country. His patient roster reads like a who's who of Hollywood and corporate America. He's an artist who sculpts human faces and bodies with such care and precision that the end result is consistently a natural and graceful appearance – "never under or over pulled".

He corrects what we had hoped nature had given us, or in some cases, what nature has taken away. Voted by his peers as one of the "Best Doctors in America," he is at the top of his field and shares the throne with his beautiful wife, who just happens to be a television celebrity in her own right.

Dr. Fisher's office is located in a medical building on a cozy, tree-lined street within the din of Beverly Hills activity. On a typical day limousines are back-to-back against the curb. An elevator takes you to the second floor where, at the termination of a private hall ensconced in marble, a hidden camera synchronized with some sort of electronic buzzer, offers those with appointments made a year in advance selective entrance. Entrance gained, you wonder if you are in a medical office or in the luxurious living room of a designer from Milan.

A cross section of human experience waits. A woman has come all the way from San Paolo, a man from New Orleans, and another woman from Singapore. It's an international gathering.

A stunning-looking woman walks through the room on her way to one of the examining suites. She pauses for a moment to chat with the receptionist. The conversation is casual, yet with a hint of intimacy. You wonder what possibly could have brought this magnificent looking female to a plastic surgeon's office. The mystique is captivating.

Then you meet Dr. Fisher. The southern accent has been assimilated (cultivated in the Mississippi Delta), but the charm remains. It becomes quite evident that he has the gift of making you feel that it is you, and you alone, who matters. It is, perhaps, part of that southern mystique, but you also know it's not phony – it's real.

Having the vision and the hands to create beauty is, obviously, a gift, just as precious as the endowment bestowed upon the classicalists of ancient Athens and Rome. This gift has led this special doctor to perform almost eight thousand surgeries in just twelve years.

A perfectionist who thoroughly enjoys his patients, Dr. Fisher is always comfortably open and honest with them. His mantra is simplistic: it is the patient who is most important. By striving to perform the surgical experience that provides the most appropriate result, he knows he has offered his best. He lets you know what you can and cannot expect, because unrealized expectations make for a disappointed patient.

The search for perfection can be a demanding taskmaster. New procedures do not necessarily yield better results. It is the surgeon's skill and judgment that make the difference, not always the latest technique or surgical gimmick. Therefore, Dr. Fisher's unsurpassed surgical selectivity creates the rejection of numerous potential patients.

The decision to undergo a cosmetic procedure can foster anxiety, fear and unrealistic expectations. The skill, honesty, integrity, and personality of the doctor are defining factors in the overall equation.

Over the years of perfecting his practice, Dr. Fisher recognized the importance of preoperative education and preparation in his patient population. This recognition became very apparent during consultations with patients who were visiting with him for second opinions. These patients seemed to lack the informational base to form educated decisions. It became clear to the doctor that an educational and informational standard of accuracy and thoroughness was missing in the field of plastic surgery. So this gifted and skilled surgeon set out to create something out of that void.

The Naked Truth About Plastic Surgery is a series of five educational videotapes designed to provide potential patients with the most comprehensive, honest and accurate information available. What began as a personal mission, and a desire to impart precise and accurate information to his own patients considering plastic surgery, has developed into one of the most incredible evolutionary educational vehicles in healthcare.

Dr. Fisher is quite clear about the fact that plastic surgery can help improve the way a person looks and feels; and recognizes that most people who visit him want to look better, have more confidence and feel better about themselves. But many people don't even know how to begin to select a qualified plastic surgeon, let alone what questions to ask during an interview or consultation process.

There is abundant information available about plastic surgery from many sources, but how do potential patients determine what is accurate and truthful; separate fact from fiction; and realistic expectations from hard-sell hype? In trying to answer those questions, Dr. Fisher became convinced that a high-class, educational series of videotapes would be an ideal way to educate about plastic surgery and help them make the right decisions regarding their own wants and needs. So he developed the videotape series, **The Naked Truth About Plastic Surgery**, designed so that a prospective candidates for a procedure could follow someone just like themselves on their own personal journey seeking reliable and truthful information.

Dr. Garth Fisher

People that view the tapes are astonished at how completely and accurately all their questions are answered. The tapes are designed to empower patients with knowledge and information so that decisions can be made in the comfort of their own homes. It eliminates the need to get the most critical information about a potential operation in a twenty-minute, face-to-face, anxiety-laden visit with their surgeon.

And the tapes belong to the patient. They can view them as often as necessary before seeking a consultation or making an informed decision. Never before has "choice" been placed so purposefully in the hands of consumers.

So empowering is this series that physicians from other specialties have joined with Dr. Fisher to develop additional series in other surgical fields.

The doctor, obviously, is a creative and gifted surgeon whose artistic craft has won praise from patient and peer alike. His most ambition gift might well be that which he imparts to a nation of consumers who require his genius more than ever.

Videotapes and videodiscs are available at www.nakedtruth.com

the beauty makers
DR. JEFFREY JOSEPH
913 South College Road #101
Lafayette, LA 70503
(337) 237-0650

Dr. Jeffrey Joseph

Every evening before Dr. Jeffrey Joseph puts his three children to bed for the night, they huddle together for a "team meeting." The four of them talk together about all sorts of things. The topics are often trivial, but to Dr. Joseph and his children the discussions are important and relevant.

"The most important thing about the team meetings are that they keep the lines of communication with my children open," he said. "And what could be more important than that?"

In a similar fashion, Dr. Joseph tries to build bridges of trust and communication with all of his patients and potential patients.

"When a patient comes in for a consultation, we spend quite a bit of time talking together about what the patient desires, what is possible and what should be done," he said. "The patient and the physician need to be on the same page, so we have to communicate with each other clearly and openly. I think this is so important that we often have patients return for multiple consultations at no extra charge."

Dr. Joseph's practice, which is in Lafayette, Louisiana, has a different atmosphere than that of a practice in a large city.

"You may be working on your child's teacher or a prominent member of the community," he said. "When you're practicing in a city this size, you see your patients all over town...at social functions, football games or at church."

But for the doctor personal attention to and concern for his patients comes naturally.

He was born in Crowley, Louisiana, a small town midway between Lake Charles and Lafayette. He attended St. Michael's School during his elementary and junior high years, and then Notre

Dame High School – where he graduated third in his class. While in school, he discovered his artistic abilities and was often involved in painting murals and posters for school activities. He was voted "Most Talented" by his graduating class.

Dr. Joseph said his parents were hard workers and instilled in him a strong work ethic. He also said his father, through sharp business sense and hard work, had become the owner of two men's clothing stores in Lafayette.

So when Dr. Joseph became old enough to work with the public, his father started him in the family business. It was while in the stores, through long days of working with the public, that he learned the art of salesmanship, how to dress and how to deal with people. But even though he demonstrated great skill in the family business, his interest gravitated toward the practice of medicine.

From early on the medical field appealed to Dr. Joseph. Two of his uncles were doctors and his brother was in medical school. So with the encouragement of his parents and other family members, he followed his interest in medicine and eventually enrolled in the School of Medicine at Louisiana State University (LSU).

Upon graduation from medical school in nineteen eighty-six, Joseph then entered and completed a residency in Otolaryngology (head and neck surgery) at LSU in New Orleans in nineteen ninety-two. Following his residency, he completed a facial plastic surgery fellowship with the American Academy of Facial Plastic and Reconstructive Surgery under Dr. William E. Silver in Atlanta, Georgia in nineteen ninety-three.

"Dr. Billy Silver was the best surgeon I have ever known," said Dr. Joseph. "He has had, and still has, a extraordinary influence on my life and practice."

During the time of his fellowship, Dr. Joseph refined his surgical techniques and gained experience in the meticulous art of facial surgery. After this valuable experience, he moved to Lake Charles, and opened his practice. Nine years later he decided to move to Lafayette and has enjoyed being "back home."

Dr. Jeffrey Joseph

When he is not practicing medicine, Dr. Joseph enjoys spending time with his children and staying active. He describes himself as a huge sports fan and tries rarely misses a New Orleans Saints or LSU football game.

To keep himself fit, Dr. Joseph said he enjoys running and tennis. When not following sports, or participating in them, he said he indulges in his creative side and exercises his innate artistic ability. He enjoys doing anything from caricatures to formal paintings. But most often, he exercises his artistic ability and his technical excellence to work with human tissue.

"Many people don't realize that you can have plastic surgery in a smaller cities like Lafayette or Lake Charles," he said. "They assume that they have to travel to Houston or New Orleans to find a surgeon. But there is no compromise in quality when they have their surgery here.

"In our city, when someone has a procedure it is not as big of a secret as it might be in a larger community. But, that's not because the surgeon or his staff betrays the confidentiality of the patient. Instead, here in this small town environment, people are more willing to talk freely about the procedures that they have had done. There seems to be a healthy attitude among our patients to talk about their experience. We get the majority of our referrals this way. I enjoy helping people make improvements to their appearance, which gives one more confidence."

Dr. Joseph said he enjoys his work and that he cares a great deal about his patients.

"I want to provide the highest level of care and professionalism possible to the people of Southwest Louisiana," he said. "I work to integrate the latest methods and technology into my practice while maintaining the personal touch that is the cornerstone of my practice. I see my patients every day, throughout the city and at social events. My patients are my friends and neighbors and I look after their best interests."

the beauty makers
DR. RENATO P. CALABRIA
436 North Bedford #200
Beverly Hills, California 90210
(310) 829-2111

Dr. Renato P. Calabria

Dr. Renato P. Calabria said that what cosmetic surgery does for an individual is to bring out "confidence and positive feeling, which is critically important because a person's self-perception is paramount to his or her achievement in life."

The internationally renowned California-based plastic surgeon, who practices in Beverly Hills, Westlake Village, Palm Desert and Rome, Italy, said nowhere can the aforementioned be seen more clearly than during his pro bono missions to Central and South America.

"Those of us who have the privilege of living in America are very lucky people," he said, "and I think it is important to give something of what we have to the less fortunate people in the world. That's why other doctors and I go on these missions...to provide our expertise and talent at no charge to people who could never afford to pay for plastic surgery."

Dr. Calabria said the majority of his surgeries in these countries are on children with congenital defects, and that there was nothing more satisfying than a mother's smile following a successful procedure.

"There's no better pay than being able to do a surgery that helps a child or an adult feel better about her or himself," he said. "Being in these countries...helping these people...is a real change of pace from Beverly Hills. It brings you back to the reality of just how wonderful our country is.

"When I'm on one of these missions, I work from six o'clock in the morning until ten o'clock at night. There's no paperwork...just the satisfaction of getting the job done, seeing the transforming power of corrective surgery, and experiencing the gratitude of the people."

The doctor, who possesses a keen sense of humor, said that when growing up in Italy he wanted to be a writer, but that his father told him to do something that would enable him to make a living – like being a doctor.

"People ask me why I practice in California," he said. "I give them the same answer Jessie James gave when he was asked why he robbed banks. It's where the money is."

He also said everybody in the field of cosmetic plastic surgery has a big ego, including himself. And Dr. Calabria said most plastic surgeons liked to think of themselves as artists, but that there was significant difference in the quality of art.

"Being Italian, I love art," he said. "I started drawing when I was young...and still do. Plastic means 'to mold,' which is like sculpting. Plastic fits my personality."

The doctor said a couple of things are critical in the field of plastic surgery.

"First of all," he said, "you have to be up-to-date on the latest techniques. A surgeon can't offer something he can't perform. Meticulous training and remaining current are vitally necessary to maintaining a state-of-the-art practice.

"Second, it's getting to the point where art is also vitally important. To get the result desired by the patient you have to have good taste and a sense of artistry. Knowledge of classical proportions is essential. A surgeon must have an innate sense of aesthetics, which is something that cannot be taught.

"An artist friend once told me that a true artist was one who could see the final result of what he was doing in his mind. One of my strengths is that I can picture what a patient is going to look like after surgery. I can see the final result in my mind."

The doctor's reputation for artistry is such that movie stars and celebrities have entrusted him to do their cosmetic surgery procedures. But, of course, his practice is not limited to high profile clientele. He performs surgeries for people from all walks of life – and in every age bracket.

"It's important to look as young as you feel," Dr. Calabria said. "Society is fixated on beauty, health and anti-aging, so many people feel the pressure to measure up to an often self-imposed standard."

Some people, he said, have unrealistic expectations as to what can be accomplished with plastic surgery.

"That's why you have to develop a good rapport with patients and be very honest with them," the doctor said. "My patients are happy with the outcome of their surgery because I'm honest with them. I listen to the patient and make an objective assessment of her or his desires…and treat each of them as the unique personality that they are."

He said that occasionally a person might desire a dramatic alteration all at once, but most patients started conservatively, which is what he advocates – gradual changes, nothing dramatic. And if someone doesn't need surgery, he tells the person they don't need it.

"I strongly object to a person getting plastic surgery to please someone else," he said. "If you're doing it to please yourself, that's OK."

A surgeon since nineteen eighty-five, Dr. Calabria began limiting his practice to plastic surgery in nineteen ninety-three because he found it more challenging than heart surgery.

"With cardiac surgery you're primarily dealing with two operations…bypass or valve…as the solution to a problem," he said. "But with plastic surgery you can have many solutions to a problem and a lot more leeway. Five different surgeons may give you five different options, which makes the field both challenging and interesting."

The most popular and minimally invasive procedure performed by Dr. Calabria is the vertical facelift with no visible scars. Others include endoscopic brow and facelift, anatomical breast enhancement, laser breast lift and reduction, laser skin resurfacing and ultrasonic liposuction.

Dr. Calabria is a graduate of the University of Padua Medical School in Italy. Postdoctoral training includes research fellowships in surgery at Harbor UCLA and Wadsworth-UCLA Medical Centers, followed by a residency in pathology at Wadsworth-UCLA. Following five years of general surgery training at Kern County-University of California San Diego Medical Center, he trained in plastic and reconstructive surgery at St. Francis Memorial Hospital in San Francisco.

Certified by The American Board of Plastic Surgery, he is also a member of The American Society of Plastic Surgery, The Los Angeles Society of Plastic Surgeons and the International Society of Plastic Surgery – and he serves on the voluntary faculty at the University of Southern California-Los Angeles, teaching residents the latest techniques in cosmetic surgery.

Dr. Calabria has, in fact, been on the faculty of numerous laser workshops in the U.S. and Europe, training other surgeons to use laser in cosmetic surgery. He has also been at the forefront of endoscopic facial plastic surgery, referred to as "minimally invasive" surgery.

Author and coauthor of numerous medical journal articles and chapters for books about plastic surgery, he has been the subject of numerous articles in U.S. and European publications. He has also been featured on numerous TV shows, both network and syndicated, in the U.S. and Europe.

Dr. Calabria, married and the father of two children, is an avid snow skier and still plays sandlot soccer with a number of friends. At one time Rod Stewart was part of the soccer bunch. He also water skis, plays tennis and was formerly a competitive swimmer.

That competitive spirit has followed him into the practice of cosmetic surgery. Whenever and wherever there are new innovations in plastic surgery, chances are that he will be right in the middle of it.

the beauty makers

the beauty makers

1-877-Gentil 4 You
www.tolookgood.com

Dr. Herve´ F. Gentile

Dr. Herve´ F. Gentile thinks the time he spent in Italy, along with his education there, profoundly affected his genius for plastic surgery especially for facial plastic surgery.

The Corpus Christi, Texas-based doctor is a third generation Italian who was born in – and grew up in – Maryland, but ended up in Italy because his parents wanted to retire there. And it was there, he said, that he became fascinated with faces and, in particular, noses.

"I think I see faces the way an artist sees faces," Dr. Gentile said, "and you can't spend time in Italy without being influenced by the art that permeates the country. In fact, I would estimate that seventy percent of the world's great art is in Italy and today Italy is recognized as a leader in style and fashion."

The country's artistic bent certainly influenced the doctor who, while living in Italy, began sculpting and painting in oils. He is an accomplished painter and sculptor, and still does both on a limited basis when his practice permits.

"A knowledge of art enables you to better understand human anatomy, and especially the face," he said. "I think it also makes you more perceptive of a patient's needs. And I think it triggered my fascination with the finer and more artistic part of plastic surgery."

The possibility to perform wonders through creativity is what drives Plastic Surgery and all of the arts and to which Dr. Gentile has always aspired.

Dr. Gentile's interest in plastic surgery matured early while studying at the University of Padua Medical School in Italy, the second oldest medical school in the world. Speaking about his educational experience in Italy, the doctor said, "The emblem chosen by the American Board of Plastic Surgery is that of Gaspare Tagliacozzi, who laid the cornerstone for modern plastic surgery by reconstructing the noses of patients in Bologna. In fifteen ninety-seven he published **De Curtorum Chirurgia per Insitionem**, which was the first textbook ever on plastic surgery."

Following his study at the medical school in Italy, Dr. Gentile returned to the United States and the University of Maryland Medical School where he completed general surgery and ear, nose and throat/head and neck surgery training. He then went to Rome, Italy to complete a fellowship in cosmetic and facial plastic surgery with Professor L. Ponti, a world-renowned plastic surgeon and early pioneer in cosmetic surgery.

"Being exposed to Dr. Ponti's office and the way he treated patients certainly influenced me," he said. "He treated patients like gods. There was a two-year waiting list of people wanting him to do their surgery.

"What's different about doctors with the same or similar skills may be in their understanding of a patient. Some doctors are very perceptive about patients and have more of a knack for understanding what they want. Dr. Ponti was like that, and I learned a great deal about the keys to understanding a patient from him. Each patient is a unique individual with unique characteristics. Therefore, a full range of alternatives and choices need to be made available and the surgeon needs to possess all the skills necessary in order to deliver each and every choice. It is this combination of knowledge, skill, talent and experience, combined with overall style that separates surgeons."

When Dr. Gentile returned to the states it was to Corpus Christi, where he practiced facial plastic surgery until he began a residency in plastic surgery at the Medical College of Georgia under the tutelage of Dr. Kenna Given, present chairman and founder of the plastic surgery program at the school and past chairman of the American Board of Plastic Surgery. Dr. Gentile currently holds an active teaching position at Medical College of Georgia as a Clinical Assistant Professor of Plastic Surgery.

Dr. Herve´ F. Gentile

The doctor's professional background also includes military service as United States Air Force flight surgeon, flying the F4 Phantom. In that capacity he had the opportunity to enjoy the "high untrespassed sanctity of space."

As a fighter pilot you experience this unique spirituality that the man and the machine become a single entity whereby it is like you put out your hand and you were able to touch the face of God. This experience also contributed towards the formation of the necessary discipline and quick decision ability required of Dr. Gentile to complete the rigorous years of residency training necessary to become a complete and well-rounded Plastic Surgeon.

When Dr. Gentile decided to build A BETTER YOU Cosmetic Surgery Center in Corpus Christi, he put his artistic abilities to work and designed it himself. It's a modern, private and environmentally friendly complex located on Ocean Drive, which winds along the beach and shoreline of the Gulf of Mexico.

"Our center is a complete in office, outpatient cosmetic plastic surgery facility," he said. "It was planned and constructed to include the most current technology and equipment available. The surgery suite was designed for the patient's comfort, convenience and privacy with all the safety features of a hospital location, but without the added expense and inconvenience of hospital care. In addition to offering laser procedures, facial peels and microdermabrasions, a new spa room has been added to complement these services.

"We maintain the highest standards and staff the center with an outstanding anesthesiology group. It's important to us that the patient feel cared for from initial consultation and through both the pre- and postoperative course."

Dr. Gentile said he and his staff attempt to develop a genuine and compassionate relationship with each patient, which, hopefully, creates a lifetime bond based upon frank communication, warmth and trust. This is created by an implacable personal commitment to the patient and her/his well-being.

"We measure our success by the number of patients who refer

their family and friends to us," he said. Since Dr. Gentile believes that God has a unique way of achieving harmony and this harmony should only be improved upon but never altered, he prefers graceful elegance and the natural look over the shock-style plastic look.

It is a myth to believe that a plastic surgeon can routinely take any face or body and make it look like someone else or that your personal life will dramatically change with plastic surgery. Just like it is a myth to believe that actresses, models, and pop stars all look great in real life (makeup and air brushing is wonderful) or that what looks commonplace in Hollywood and New York City often looks good.

Dr. Gentile 's tip is that if you seek plastic surgery, yes, you can expect to improve your looks and raise your self esteem, but you must be prepared to have realistic expectations and spend time searching for your choice of the right surgeon and there are many surgeons practicing cosmetic surgery without proper qualifications. Dr. Gentile believes that unnatural and unfavorable results often occur when unskilled or incompetent surgeons try to perform the appropriate operation or when adequately trained surgeons perform the inappropriate operation.

Dr. Gentile said Corpus Christi could not be compared to cities such as New York and San Francisco, where there is seemingly no end to the number of wealthy patients seeking plastic surgery. Today it has become very affordable for everyone. There is a plethora of financial companies specializing in offering their services to patients desiring cosmetic surgery. Tomorrow everything can happen and we all desire to be there and at the same time look and feel the best. This is why I feel cosmetic surgery in the future can only get better.

The doctor, who is triple American Board certified in Facial Plastic Surgery, Plastic Surgery and ENT/Head and Neck Surgery said, "I've dedicated myself to the highest standards of the art of plastic surgery, but I never forget the human need."

To that end he donates a portion of his time to the local children's hospital, doing cleft lip and palate surgery and reconstructing other congenital deformities on infants as young as three to four days old. There is nothing more gratifying then being able to restore a more normal function to a child or a baby, and see his smile some years later. Ultimately this is what Dr. Gentile's thinks is his purpose in life.

the beauty makers
DR. JEFFREY S. EPSTEIN
6280 Sunset Drive #508
Miami, Florida 33143
(305) 666-5884

Dr. Jeffrey S. Epstein

merica can be thankful for the dedicated, gifted, medical professionals prevalent in our society. Our nation offers some of the best medical care in the world and those who forge milestones in medicine are worthy of our applause.

One professional who has earned such accolades is Jeffrey S. Epstein, M.D, F.A.C.S., a leader in facial plastic and reconstructive surgery and an internationally recognized expert in the field of hair restoration. Dr. Epstein's devotion to his profession, passion for perfection, and innate aesthetic skills has led him to the forefront of his field. His success in the specialty of treating hair loss has won him accolades from patients and the admiration of his peers.

Born forty years ago in New York, Dr. Epstein discovered early on the path that would lead him to his career. "As a child, I discovered that I liked to work with my hands," he said. "I learned to play the violin at an early age and it continues to be a hobby. Working with my hands inspired me to learn a craft. The lure to become a surgeon, using my hands to work on people, became an early preoccupation. It took me to medical school, then on to plastic surgery limited to the face, then to my ultimate area of specialization, hair restoration."

Dr. Epstein's academic credentials are more than impressive. After completing medical training at the University of Vermont College of Medicine, he continued studying in the areas of head and neck surgery/otolaryngology (ear, nose and throat) at the University of Miami/Jackson Memorial Hospital. The American Academy of Facial Plastic and Reconstructive Surgery then awarded him a fellowship. "I hadn't yet chosen my sub-specialty," he reported, "but one of my professors who served as my mentor helped me make the choice.

He offered me a suggestion that would lead me in the right direction, advising me to master one thing and do it better than anyone else.

"If I were you," he said, "I would learn to do hair."

Those words had a lasting effect, motivating Dr. Epstein and pointing him in the right direction.

The doctor continued his fellowship studies in California's San Francisco Bay area, then earned the highest score on the Facial Plastic Surgery board exams and won the board's coveted Jack Anderson Memorial Award. In nineteen ninety-four he returned to Miami, devoting his practice to facial cosmetic surgery and specializing in hair restoration. He serves as a member of the elite International Alliance of Hair Restoration Surgeons (IAHRS), a group of just twenty-eight highly skilled surgeons from around the world. Dr. Epstein, along with other experts in the field, is convinced that the state-of-the-art treatment for baldness lies in transplantation, a low risk surgical procedure that for the doctor has become an art.

Dr. Epstein is unique in the field of hair transplantation, where his background in facial plastic surgery provides him with an aesthetic eye. He has become one of the world's few doctors performing hair restoration via all the techniques available, including follicular unit micro grafting, mega session transplantation, hair restoration for women, reparative procedures, and the repair of scalp reduction and scalp flap procedures. By offering a variety of treatments, Dr. Epstein is able to apply the correct techniques for each patient, tailoring treatment to best meet a patient's needs.

"Estimates tell us that over fifty percent of men will experience hair loss," he said. "That's over fifty million men, plus another ten million women who will suffer disturbing hair loss. The problem is primarily due to genetics, inherited traits within the family. Prevention is, therefore, unavailable. The few hair loss-inhibiting medications on the market unfortunately have only limited efficacy. That's not encouraging to those millions who are destined to lose their hair," Dr. Epstein said.

Dr. Jeffrey S. Epstein

Since nineteen ninety-four he has served as director of his Miami-based Foundation for Hair Restoration. "At the Foundation," the doctor explained, "We embrace a single dedicated mission. We are committed to providing hair restoration in an ethical, professional, and safe environment." In addition to his busy clinical practice, Dr. Epstein is a clinical voluntary professor at the University of Miami College of Medicine, and is well published in the medical literature.

The Foundation provides more than clinical therapy and surgical procedures. Dr. Epstein has made it a clearing-house of knowledge, offering patients' up-to-date information about hair loss and all the specialized techniques available to treat it. Those interested can access the Foundation's WEB site (www.foundhair.com) to explore the topic in depth before making an appointment for consultation.

Dr. Epstein explained why his Foundation has achieved success. "Our emphasis is on establishing a solid doctor-patient relationship, which will help guide the patient through the entire hair restoration process. An individualized treatment plan is assured for every patient, and I personally perform or supervise each segment of treatment and follow-up. "Success in hair transplantation requires a surgeon with a trained hand to create the most natural appearing result that mimics Mother Nature and is undetectable to even the most critical eye."

Dr. Epstein's concern for the individual patient is his first priority. "Patients need to approach hair restoration for the right reasons," he explained. "They must understand that like any cosmetic surgery, it's designed to improve a feature, but if they are seeking a total transformation, or are seeking treatment to make someone else happy, those are the wrong reasons. They are setups for failure. My job is to restore patients' hair that, hopefully, will make them feel better about themselves. Hair loss or baldness attacks the ego and can, at times, weaken self-confidence. For professional men and women it can be debilitating to the degree that their careers suffer. The decision to take action against hair loss can be, for some, a difficult one. By choosing the most qualified hair restoration expert, the decision becomes an easier one to make. Hair restoration lasts a lifetime. It needs to be done by an expert, someone who, through his experience and the quality of the hair restorations performed on his patients, inspires confidence."

Dr. Epstein encourages his patients to educate themselves about hair loss and hair restoration. "I refer them to my WEB site, where they can learn all about the condition and the procedures used to correct it. By educating themselves, they gain confidence, knowing what to expect from the treatment and how it is applied. I explain to each patient precisely how he or she will be treated and what results to expect. I work with a team of professionals, directing their efforts through each phase of the restoration procedure. There have been some challenging cases," the doctor explained. "There are definite challenges in those patients with scarring or who have had bad procedures performed. Unfortunately there is a host of unqualified hair loss specialists who offer procedures that can cause more harm than good."

Dr. Epstein's patients have offered words of praise for his skillful treatment. An individual who had undergone several unsuccessful procedures in the past said, "Dr. Epstein is an artist and a genius...I am so happy to have hair and have it look so incredibly natural. I feel I have been given back my freedom." A commercial pilot had similar accolades. "I am really pleased with the results. My wife says I look 10 years younger." A female banker also praised Dr. Epstein's work. "The doctor was caring, and took the time to discuss with me all the options. Having chosen to go with hair transplants to treat my thinning hair, after the second procedure my hair is even thicker than after the first procedure." A trial attorney offered further kudos. "Since Dr. Epstein's surgery, my self-esteem and youthful vigor have been refreshed. It is very painful to admit, but the male ego seems to be directly connected to the top of your head. Dr. Epstein's miraculous work is a cure-all for the ailing male ego. He can turn back the hands of time."

Dr. Jeffrey S. Epstein

Dr. Epstein takes special satisfaction from the praises of his patients and finds intense fulfillment in helping them. "I'm rewarded each time I successfully restore someone's hair or enhance their appearance through cosmetic surgery," the doctor reported. "In restoring hair, correcting faults, removing blemishes, and eliminating unkind scars, I feel like I'm helping nature just as nature helps us all through the healing process. It's the reason why I face the challenge of each new patient's needs, to offer my skills with helping hands, getting things perfect."

Although seriously dedicated, Dr. Epstein's interests are not limited to his craft. He is active in community affairs, serves on a private school board, and is involved with charity work. He enjoys a warm family life with his wife and three children, and an active devotion to tennis. His demeanor is quiet, confident, and reserved but that may be misleading. "Inside, I'm a lot more intense than I appear," Epstein confesses. "I search for perfection in both my professional and personal life. I want to achieve great lasting relationships with associates, patients, family, and friends. I find self-fulfillment in that, and in a great game of tennis – that's Nirvana for me."

the beauty makers
DR.KRISTON KENT
1660 Medical Blvd. #100
Naples, FL 34110
941-514-7888

Dr. Kriston Kent

Growing up in a household where both parents were college professors encouraged Dr. Kriston Kent's love of learning. His father was a biology professor and his mother a professor of mathematics. He said that through their example and active involvement in his education they instilled in him a love of knowledge and prepared him for a lifetime of learning.

Those gifts served Dr. Kent well as he prepared himself for a career in medicine – and they serve him well today.

Kent said he was interested in medicine at an early age. With the encouragement and support of his parents, he was a volunteer in the local hospital's emergency room while in high school. He spent time with the doctors, asked them questions and learned by observation. Through this involvement he said that he decided the best way for him to make a difference in the world was to practice medicine.

The doctor graduated from the University of North Alabama, first in his class, with a degree in Professional Biology. A few years later he graduated Cum Laude from the University of Alabama School of Medicine.

While in medical school Dr. Kent was chapter president of Alpha Omega the medical honor society that comprises the top ten percent of medical students. After medical school, he served a fellowship through the American Academy of Facial Plastic and Reconstructive Surgery at the Mangat Plastic Surgery Center in Cincinnati, Ohio.

Dr. Kent has dual board certifications in both Facial Plastic Surgery and Otolaryngology and in two thousand one was appointed by the governor of Florida to serve on the Florida Board of Medicine. He has also served as president elect of the Florida Society of Facial Plastic and Reconstructive Surgery.

Though the doctor said he finds his practice rewarding and stimulating, he said the joy of his life is his wife Charlotte, a computer systems analyst, and their three children – Kristi, Allen and Aimee.

The family, he said, is very active, so he spends a lot of time involved in the academic and sporting interests of his wife and children.

Dr. Kent said he is an avid runner and also said he and his family enjoy hiking when they vacation. He also enjoys the tired satisfaction of physical labor.

"Growing up on a farm gives you an appreciation for doing constructive work with your hands," he said.

The doctor serves as an elder in his church, collects for the Leukemia Foundation, supports missionary work and assists a local shelter for abused women.

"I want to inspire others to find the best within themselves," he said. "I don't want to be some sort of self-appointed leader, but a person who is worth following."

His wife and friends say the doctor is his harshest critic.

"I'm something of a perfectionist," he admitted. "I'm rarely completely satisfied with my work. I always want to have everything work out perfectly with no scars at all and absolutely no signs of surgery but that's not realistic. I suppose it is part of my artistic nature."

Dr. Kent's idealism carries through to his philosophy of patient care.

"We want to do the best we can and to exceed the patient's expectations," he said. "The great thing about doing facial plastic surgery is that we get to know our patients as people. We don't have to see a large number of patients each day, so there's time to relax and get to know a patient."

The doctor said his rapport with patients is natural and easy.

"My father grew up in a country store and learned how to make conversation with just about anyone," he said. "He knew how to make them feel at ease. I seem to have learned to do the same thing through his example. "I think it's important for the patients to know their surgeon and to understand and feel comfortable with the procedures. It gives them confidence in me and in themselves."

Of course, there is every reason for Dr. Kent's patients to have confidence in him. When his Naples, Florida practice opened in nineteen ninety, he was, he said, the first board-certified facial plastic surgeon in the city. His Naples Facial Plastic Surgery center has been very successful and has achieved a strong reputation through his commitment to excellence.

The surgeon said he fulfills that commitment through his dedication to being a lifelong student. He spends hundreds of hours each year in structured continuing education as well as untold hours doing private research and reading of the latest medical journals to keep up with the latest developments in his discipline of medicine. Dr. Kent regularly teaches his colleagues around the country the latest advances in Facial Plastic and Reconstructive Surgery. His national specialty society, the American Academy of Facial Plastic and Reconstructive Surgery (AAFPRS), is the leading society of specialty Plastic Surgery in the U.S. Through the AAFPRS foundation, education and philanthropy are the primary focuses of its activities. Dr. Kent is active in both endeavors. He is also affiliated with the University of Florida School of Medicine's Department of Otolaryngology/Division of Facial Plastic and Reconstructive Surgery.

While all of that studying, research, and many hours spent involved in societies and teaching would be boring to some people, Dr. Kent sees it as both challenging and necessary.

"It helps me do a better job of helping my patients," he said, "and that's what it's all about isn't it? Besides, I love what I do. I look forward to going to work each day. What could be better?"

the beauty makers
DR. RONALD J. CANIGLIA
7102 East Acoma Drive
Scottsdale, Arizona 85254
(480) 483-1702

Dr. Ronald J. Caniglia

When he was a child he had an interest in first aid and in helping other people – an interest that manifested itself in his choice of a profession.

"I remember as a child reading books on how to treat accident victims and trauma patients," Dr. Ronald J. Caniglia said. "Being intrigued with such things at an early age, the idea of becoming a doctor seemed very natural.

"And because I've always loved art and working with my hands...combined with my creative ability and love of aesthetics and beauty...it's probably not surprising that I chose the field of facial plastic surgery. My choosing to specialize in plastic surgery of the face was because it is very precise, tedious surgery requiring tremendously fine motor skills and a keen aesthetic eye for beauty and symmetry. It's the kind of art that I love doing."

The Scottsdale, Arizona-based surgeon said he is a strong believer in preoperative treatment of the skin prior to undergoing facial surgery, along with postoperative maintenance of the surgical result.

"We have a full service day spa, Bella Palage Spa, which assists all my patients in both the pre- and postoperative care of their skin. We also use a lot of natural herbs, vitamins and nutritional supplements to assist our patients."

When considering cosmetic surgery it is important, the doctor said, to be sure what you want the surgery to accomplish.

"I recommend thoroughly researching the procedure you're contemplating," he said, "and strongly recommend multiple consultations with several physicians. I can't emphasize enough the importance of choosing a surgeon who specializes in the procedure you decide on. A quality plastic surgeon will gladly show you before and after photographs of his or her patients…and will not object to your talking to patients on whom he or she has performed the same type surgery you are contemplating."

Board certification is important, Dr. Caniglia said, but it can be misleading.

"Contrary to some boards reporting that they are exclusive in certifying plastic surgeons," he said, "it's important to know that multiple boards do certification. Instead of getting caught up in trying to determine who has what type of certification, just be sure your physician has privileges at a local hospital to perform the procedure you're contemplating. If your doctor has those privileges, he or she has the proper training and board certification."

Dr. Caniglia said prior to surgery he wanted a patient to fully understand the procedure he would be performing, to be knowledgeable about his skills, to feel comfortable with him as a person and to also be comfortable with his staff.

"My attitude toward a patient is that he or she is my most important patient," he said, "and that he or she is guaranteed my absolute best at all times no matter how simple or complex the procedure. My goal is to provide every patient with a positive and rewarding experience, and to ensure that all my patients are completely satisfied with all aspects of their care.

"I'm hopeful that my patients, my staff and other physicians perceive me not only as an excellent surgeon, but also as a man of integrity, ethics, honor and sound morals."

Asked what he considered to be the most important features in a woman's beauty, the doctor said, "Women tend to have more overall defined brow, cheek and jaw lines than men. They also have softer body curves than men. However, I think it's the eyes and brow complex that are among the most important features in determining the beauty of a woman."

Dr. Caniglia said his most difficult and unusual cases are usually complicated reconstructive rhinoplasties.

"In these particular cases," he said, "it's a matter of working with every medium of the body…skin, muscle, fatty tissue, bone and cartilage. And you're often adding additional grafts, both autologous and synthetic, to try and reconstruct the nose and mold it to a more acceptable shape…and to help the nose function better in its capacity."

The doctor is a native of Omaha, Nebraska, graduated from Westside High School there, then earned his B.S. degree from the University of Nebraska at Lincoln and his medical degree from the University of Nebraska Medical Center in Omaha. Following a one-year internship in general surgery at Wesley Medical Center in Wichita, Kansas, he returned to Omaha and the Nebraska Medical Center for a four-year stint in otolaryngology surgery. He then did a one-year fellowship through the American Academy of Facial Plastic and Reconstructive Surgery at Perkins Facial Plastic Surgery in Indianapolis, Indiana.

He considers Dr. Steven Perkins, along with his parents, as major influences in the building of his career.

"Dr. Perkins was a tremendous inspiration and provided me a wealth of knowledge," he said. "And my parents continually encouraged and supported me."

After a year and a half with an otolaryngology practice in the Phoenix/Scottsdale area of Arizona, where his focus was facial plastic surgery, Dr. Caniglia opened his own practice in late fall of nineteen ninety-four. Four years later he built and opened The Caniglia Center, which is a fifteen thousand-square foot ambulatory surgery center and day spa.

"Opening The Caniglia Center fulfilled a lifelong dream," he said. "Watching the construction of that dream, which I helped design, and now being able to practice in it daily is tremendously rewarding."

A hard worker from the time he was a young child, he was a busboy at the "Here's Johnny" Restaurant at thirteen. At fifteen, he worked at a lawn care center. And during summer months when in high school he worked at the Kellogg's cereal factory in his hometown.

"After graduating college, I worked briefly at an alcohol and drug counseling center," the doctor said. "And to help pay my way through medical school, I worked two jobs. One was managing a moderate size apartment complex and the other was performing history and physical examinations on patients for local doctors at an area hospital."

Most people think of Dr. Caniglia as relaxed and low key, but those who know him best also consider him to be very much a "Type A" personality – a perfectionist in every respect.

The doctor, a practicing Catholic, said the birth of each of his children ranked among the happiest moments in his life – that and sharing every growing moment with them.

"It's a remarkable process, watching these children grown and learn," he said. "I'm involved in a number of extracurricular activities, but my family occupies much of that time. With three young boys who are involved in nearly every sport, weekends are spent going to various athletic contests. As a family we also enjoy biking, golf, snow skiing, traveling and fine dining."

Dr. Caniglia is heavily involved in the American Academy of Facial Plastic and Reconstructive Surgery (AAFPRS), and serves on several committees. He is involved with numerous local charities and, with his wife and another friend, co-chaired a major fundraiser for Phoenix Children's Hospital in two thousand two. He also works with the AAFPRS Domestic Violence Abuse Program, providing free services to women who have been abused.

"Our national academy is continually striving to educate the public about the specifics of our training and expertise, and about the various procedures available to them," he said. "Because members provide their services free of charge to abused women and underprivileged children worldwide, the academy is making an international impact."

The doctor called the future of plastic surgery "exciting."

"There's a tremendous push towards anti-aging and prevention of the aging process," he said. "We are currently incorporating many anti-aging protocols into the care of our patients.

"Life is a gift, extremely precious, and we must enjoy every possible moment of it. We are all here for a reason. We all have opportunity to help each other, to become better persons and to build a better world. My gift is to help those who seek facial rejuvenation or reconstruction…and I experience joy through their eyes."

the beauty makers
DR. JIM GILMORE
6750 Hillcrest Plaza Dr. #215
Dallas, TX 75230
972-960-0950

Dr. Jim Gilmore

Dr. Jim Gilmore said that prior to becoming involved with the "Face To Face" program, he was not fully aware of the travesty and magnitude of domestic violence.

The doctor is a facial plastic and cosmetic surgeon who has an internationally known practice in Dallas, Texas and "Face To Face" is a humanitarian and educational surgical exchange program conducted under the sponsorship of the Educational and Research Foundation for the American Academy of Facial Plastic and Reconstructive Surgery (AAFPRS) in cooperation with the National Domestic Violence Project. Dr. Gilmore has been involved with the program since it was founded in 1992.

"Facial plastic surgery can be an important step for the survivor to rebuild her self-esteem and remove the daily physical reminder of the abuse she endured," he said. "A great need exists for the skills of a facial plastic surgeon, and I feel good about using my skills and giving my time back to others in society, particularly those in such need."

Dr. Gilmore said he invests a substantial amount of his time and money into his community. He works with the Women's Shelter, the "I Have A Dream" program, the Dallas Ronald McDonald House and the Breastmobile. He is also a member of the Kiwanis Club.

Through these groups he said he joins with others to meet the most urgent needs of the community, but said he does not confine his involvement to simply the most basic needs. He also promotes and supports groups that improve the lifestyle of the community, serving on the board of directors for the Dallas Civic Opera, the Dallas Museum of Art, the Dallas Nature Center, the Town North

YMCA and the Richardson Symphony Orchestra. He also financially supports the Dallas Symphony Association, the Sierra Club and the Stephen F. Austin State University Alumni Association.

Between spending time with family, community service and the demands of his practice, the doctor regularly participates in seminars and workshops both nationally and internationally. He has been a visiting consultant in his specialty in many areas of the world including Brazil, China, India, France and Viet Nam. In addition, he is often consulted by the print and television media as a resource for answers about the procedures and ethics of cosmetic surgery.

Dr. Gilmore, born and raised near Palestine, Texas, originally wanted to be a soldier. While in high school he sought appointment to West Point through the congressman who represented the district in which he lived, but said he was unable to get the appointment because of political differences and the relative lack of advanced classes in the public school system he attended. He took the advice of the congressman and attended Texas A&M University to take courses that would improve his status as a candidate for appointment to West Point.

While at A&M, he took classes in the premed program as a means of gaining advanced science classes for his transcript. The more he learned about medicine, the more interested he became in becoming a doctor. He soon abandoned the idea of a military career and decided to complete his premed studies and attend the University of Texas Southwestern Medical School.

In medical school, Dr. Gilmore often assisted in surgery and finally decided to become a surgeon.

"Surgery fit my skills and mental abilities," he said.

After graduation from medical school, he was drafted into the United States Air Force where he served as a surgeon and obstetrician.

Following service in the Air Force, Dr. Gilmore's private practice has included treatment of the ear, nose and throat as well as cosmetic and plastic surgery. Over the years, he said he has narrowed his practice to cosmetic surgery.

He said that his varied background has enabled him to create a powerful combination of experience, education and professionalism in the delicate area of cosmetic surgery. And, although he keeps up with the latest advances in cosmetic surgery, he said he is conservative when it comes to recommending procedures for his patients. He prefers smaller, subtler adjustments that sculpt the body rather than major surgeries that significantly alter the appearance.

Dr. Gilmore contends that a good cosmetic and plastic surgeon needs to have an eye for beauty and an appreciation for art in its purest form. Skill, alone, he said, is simply not enough.

"Asymmetry is a part of each person's uniquely natural beauty," he said. "If our faces were completely symmetrical, they would look completely unnatural. Here lives the surgical challenge…to improve upon the face's natural asymmetry and maintain an illusion of facial balance. It is not an exact art, nor should it be viewed as such, but rather as a careful system of surgical sculpting that deals with delicate human structure."

The doctor is currently practicing a procedure he calls "the internal facelift." He said the internal facelift combines several less invasive procedures and has a quicker recovery with improved results.

"During a facelift we must correct sagging skin and muscles, so lifting just the skin does not always give the best results," the surgeon said. "We must go deeper and treat beneath the skin as well. That's what the internal facelift does."

Dr. Gilmore said the key to providing a firmer, more youthful face lies underneath the skin.

"Gravity is not the only cause of loose skin on the face," he said. "Looseness can also be cause by shrinkage of the underlying bone and fat. Therefore, the first step in the internal facelift is to remodel or reconstruct the face internally, using a variety of specialized, high technology implants."

The implants, he said, are followed by endoscopic and laser surgery that lifts the skin, making it smoother and firmer. The tiny incisions are concealed in the hairline and around the ears, leaving no visible scars.

"The result is natural looking, not stretched or overly tight," Dr. Gilmore said.

The surgeon explained that because the internal facelift is a combination of several less-invasive procedures, rather than one major surgical procedure, the recovery is quicker and more comfortable. He said the patient will feel little pain or discomfort after the surgery and can wear make-up immediately.

"While there may be some swelling the first day following surgery, there is no redness or bruising," Dr. Gilmore said. "Once the swelling goes down, which takes about one day, the face will be completely healed and look years younger.

"Although the desire to combat the aging process and to remake their appearance is unique to every person, during various decades of our life the desire to make certain changes in appearances is governed by our life situation and our age and maturity level. Many times, even a simple procedure like changing the nose that you never liked gives a tremendous self-confidence boost."

While many procedures may be beneficial for a patient, Dr. Gilmore stresses that it is important for a patient to consult honestly and specifically with a surgeon to discuss what can be realistically achieved through cosmetic surgery.

"We have always believed that a patient's full and complete understanding of what can be expected from cosmetic and plastic surgery and from their surgeon is critical to a successful outcome," he said. "You don't want to look like you have had cosmetic surgery. Your natural anatomy will stay the same. I always work with the natural art of the body. Natural aesthetic beauty stands the test of time."

the beauty makers

the beauty makers
DR. KARL J. EISBACH
7800 Constitution Ave. NE
Albuquerque, NM 87110
505-332-7800

Dr. Karl J. Eisbach

Dr. Karl J. Eisbach has a thriving nationwide facial plastic surgery practice, placing him in the top five-percent nationally, for the number of facial plastic procedures he performs annually. This statistic is even more amazing when you consider that Dr. Eisbach's practice is located in the high desert of Albuquerque, New Mexico - one of the country's least populated states.

Uniquely located just an hour's flight from the major metropolis of Los Angeles, Denver, Phoenix, and Dallas, New Mexico offers an incomparable place to recover from surgery. In fact, New Mexico has a long history of people traveling to the state for its restorative spirit and climate. No wonder that this surgeon identified this state as a place for a national cosmetic practice.

Dr. Eisbach specializes in all types of facial plastic surgery procedures with an emphasis on rhinoplasty (noses) and facial rejuvenation. Referrals from physicians and satisfied patients are the keystone of his busy practice. He is highly skilled in achieving a natural unoperated appearance in facelifts by carefully protecting the hairline and/or beard line using his own specially developed surgical techniques, which minimize scarring. This is particularly significant when people are having multiple procedures and with the rapid growth of the male component of his practice.

Double boarded in Facial Plastic Surgery and ENT, he is an expert in the aesthetics and function of the face which permits better results in facial procedures, such as nose surgery, that demand a cosmetic change as well as preserving and/or improving airway function.

In addition to his private practice, Dr. Eisbach has been a clinical assistant professor at the University of New Mexico School of Medicine for more than twenty years. He has an appointment in the

Division of Otolaryngology (treatment of diseases, injuries or abnormalities that affect the head and neck) and Plastic Surgery. In that capacity he teaches young physicians both the art of medicine and the importance of serving their patients.

Furthering his desire to share his skills and teach facial plastic surgery, Dr. Eisbach is the Director of a Facial Plastic Surgery Fellowship Program - one of only thirty-eight in the world. This competitive one-year experience allows a fully trained surgeon to get advanced training with an expert in the field. "I find teaching to be stimulating and it keeps me on my toes," states Dr. Eisbach.

Dr. Eisbach asserts that plastic surgery, once thought of as a luxury of the rich and famous, is now fairly common for people of every economic status. "It's not just corporate executives and celebrities who seek plastic surgery today," he comments. "Teachers, more than any other profession, make up the highest number of facial plastic surgery patients." Recent statistics show that two-thirds of people who have cosmetic surgery have family incomes of less than fifty thousand dollars a year. "The reasons are easy to understand," he says. "We're living longer, staying more active, and having multiple careers. Consequently, people want to look as good as they feel. And, alternatively, people often feel better when they look better."

Dr. Eisbach, of course, says he does not want anyone to think that facial plastic surgery is a trivial matter. He and his team consult carefully and thoroughly with each patient to determine the needs and desires of that patient and to help her or him make the appropriate decision about facial surgery. "Fortunately," he states, "today's surgical techniques rarely require a hospital stay or a lengthy recovery."

"We have a state-of-the-art, fully certified, award winning facility, which provides a safe, warm and caring, yet very confidential, atmosphere for our patients of which we are very proud," shares Dr. Eisbach. "And our staff works extremely hard to make the experience as comfortable and secure as possible. We want to ensure that our patients receive personal attention and that they feel completely at ease with everything we do for them."

Dr. Karl J. Eisbach

The surgeon remarks that for he and his team the overall health of a patient is the top priority. Dr. Eisbach says, "It's more than just surgery. Beyond the procedures, we want to help our patients establish better habits for taking care of themselves...their skin and their health...drinking lots of water, not smoking, sun protection, exercise, and good skin care techniques. If a person decides to have a procedure, we want to help them extend the benefits of it by practicing good health habits."

Dr. Eisbach believes, "The main key to my success is a dedication to providing the best possible results and experience for our patients and surrounding them with sensitive caring people. That starts with providing a very clear and honest consultation. I live by the motto that you never promise more than you can deliver and that you always deliver more than you promise.

"The second key is to continue improving our techniques and services so we constantly get better," Dr. Eisbach notes. "That's why I put my professional energies into reading, attending workshops, and reviewing the most current procedures and techniques."

This quest for excellence is substantiated by continual feedback from both patients and physicians. In fact, as founder and former Chairman of the Cosmetic and Reconstructive Surgery Department at Lovelace Medical Center, Dr. Eisbach's practice was consistently rated the highest in patient satisfaction for the entire 300 plus physician medical center.

Though the days of a surgeon are often long and the work is precise and demanding, Dr. Eisbach always finds it very rewarding because he has the opportunity to work with the intricacy of the human face. "I've always had good dexterity in both hands and what they call a 'good touch'. This combined with the genuine joy he gets from working one on one with his patients translates into a highly energized and successful practice. "I like doing facial surgery because even subtle changes can make a significant difference in how a person feels about himself or herself. Helping people look and feel better often translates into improved self-esteem and confidence."

Dr. Eisbach affirms that many people who seek facial surgery are dealing with sensitive emotional issues. Their lives have been affected because of the way that they, and often their peers, perceive their appearance. "Even careless or cruel words that are spoken on the school playground affect some of my patients into their adult life," notes Dr. Eisbach. "How your peers treat you can have a profound effect on your entire life."

But even with such an extensive practice, Dr. Eisbach has found time, through the American Academy of Facial Plastic and Reconstructive Surgery "Face to Face" program, to organize and lead multiple trips to Central America to perform plastic surgery.

"In Central America you see all sorts of things that you would never see in the United States," he says. "Since many children don't even have basic medical care, you see large tumors, or heavy, disfiguring scarring from burns. It is also common to see eight- or nine-year-old children with a cleft lip or cleft palate." Over the past few years, Dr. Eisbach's medical teams to Central America have treated more than three hundred children with cleft lips or cleft palates. Drug companies and medical suppliers often donate the drugs, equipment and supplies for this charitable work, but the surgeons who participate pay all other costs.

Dr. Eisbach credits his strong work ethic, to his parents who taught him that no job is too menial to do and to do it well. He credits his wife, Jeri Peterson, for making a more active commitment to volunteerism. "Her quiet, personal commitment to helping the less fortunate has always had a subtle but profound influence on the scope and depth of my volunteer activities."

When he can escape the demands of his practice, Dr. Eisbach enjoys spending time with his family and staying active. "I grow great tomatoes, usually six or seven varieties," he states with pride. He enjoys the physical labor and mental relaxation that working in the garden provides.

He is also an aspiring chef and wine enthusiast who specializes in chocolate creations - much to his wife's delight. And to keep fit and mentally sharp, he enjoys cycling, race walking and skiing. "And, in New Mexico that can always be an interesting experience," he says, like running into a mountain lion on one of his morning walks. "He went one way and I went the other – fast."

Dr. Eisbach finds that life brings him great joy and there is much he wants to do and share with others. His wife says he smiles a lot and is very upbeat . . . "he has a lot of energy and even though he is constantly going, he always seems to have time for his patients, staff, family and friends."

While the doctor's practice gives him a great deal of satisfaction, he still reflects on the memories of the Central American children that he and his team have been able to help through the years. He recalled a situation where a family had rejected their nine-year-old boy because of his cleft lip. The boy was on his own in the world, his self-esteem nearly nonexistent because of his birth defect. Dr. Eisbach said he and his team had the privilege of repairing the boy's lip and seeing him restored to his family.

"We take a lot of things for granted," he remarks, "but experiences like that make you realize what is important. And how profoundly appearance can affect the quality of life in any culture and/or economic level."

the beauty makers
DR. ROBERT L. SIMONS, MD
16800 NW 2nd Avenue – Suite 607
N. Miami Beach, Florida 33169
(305) 651-9903

Dr. Robert L. Simons

Dr. Robert L. Simons, an internationally recognized authority on facial plastic and reconstructive surgery, initially planned to be a lawyer. His decision to become a physician was the legal profession's loss and the medical profession's gain.

Dr. Simons was born in Philadelphia, Pennsylvania. He was an excellent student, became president of his high school class, and earned a BA degree in English from Dickinson College in nineteen fifty-seven. He was admitted to Medical School at the University of Pennsylvania based strictly on his abilities.

Following graduation from medical school in nineteen sixty-one, he began a rotating internship and pediatric residency at Children's Hospital in Philadelphia in nineteen sixty-two, which is where he became interested in otolaryngology. This led to a residency at Mount Sinai Hospital in New York City beginning in nineteen sixty-four. By this time he knew he was much more interested in otolaryngology than in pediatrics.

At Mount Sinai, Dr. Simons was greatly influenced by two men – Dr. Joseph Goldman, chairman of the otolaryngology department, and Dr. Irving Goldman, a master rhinoplasty surgeon and teacher. The former was politically involved with the formation of the American Academy of Facial Plastic and Reconstructive Surgery (AAFPRS) and the latter became the first president of the organization in nineteen sixty-four.

"Dr. Irving Goldman had a dedication to teaching that captured my attention and provoked a passion in me for rhinoplasty," says Dr. Simons.

And, in his department Dr. Joseph Goldman allowed the teacher and residents the freedom to discover what aspects of surgery interested them.

"Maybe five- to ten-percent of head and neck surgeons go into plastic surgery," Dr. Simons says. He also says that during a two-year stint in the Army he learned how to do much more than noses.

The doctor founded The Simons Center for Nasal and Facial Plastic Surgery in Miami in nineteen seventy-three, and has practiced in the Florida city for some thirty years. Since nineteen ninety-one he has served as a director of the Division of Facial Plastic and Reconstructive Surgery for the University of Miami School of Medicine, where he has been a faculty member since nineteen seventy-four. He is certified by the American Board of Otolaryngology and by the American Board of Facial Plastic and Reconstructive Surgery (ABFPRS).

Dr. Simons is past president of the AAFPRS and in nineteen eighty-nine helped edit the book, **Coming of Age: A History of the AAFPRS**, commemorating the academy's twenty-fifth anniversary. His work has been published in various professional publications, including the Archives of Otolaryngology, The Facial Plastic Clinics of North America and The AMA Archives of Facial Plastic Surgery. He served as president of the ABFPRS from nineteen ninety-one to ninety-four and frequently lectures at medical meetings and symposiums throughout the country and abroad.

An integral part of the doctor's professional life has been and is his political involvement and teaching, and his active and ardent support for the development of plastic surgery has spanned several decades. In the late sixties he became a member of AAFPRS and an active teaching member at the Goldman Course. And, in nineteen seventy, he became the first surgeon other than Dr. Goldman to operate at the popular June rhinoplasty meeting. For more than twenty-five years thereafter he, along with Drs. Sidney Feurestein, Bill Lawson, Irvin Fine and Sam Bloom, carried on the Mount Sinai course tradition.

Dr. Simons' abiding interest in the growth of AAFPRS is evidenced by the time he has devoted to elective office; southern regional vice president in nineteen seventy-five and seventy-six, national program chairman in nineteen seventy-seven, treasurer from nineteen seventy-nine through nineteen eighty-three, and president in nineteen eighty-five and eighty-six. While president he recognized the accomplishments of the past, but emphasized the need for a stronger future identity. An endowment program was initiated with Dr. John Conley's one hundred thousand dollar gift, the Founders Club was organized and the Past Presidents Club established.

For well over a decade Dr. Simons has worked with equal fervor to ensure the success of the ABFPRS. Following his service as the board's secretary in nineteen eighty-eight, he began a three-year term as the board's president in nineteen ninety-two.

He also helped develop the publication **Facial Plastic Times**, and served as its editor from nineteen eighty through eighty-five.

Today, as Chairman of the Fellowship Examination Corporation Leadership Society, he continues to be an active member of ABFPRS and, along with Dr. Devinder Mangat, has co-chaired the joint Capital Campaign, which has helped raise more than three million dollars for facial plastic surgery.

Dr. Simons has been the recipient of various AAFPRS honors, including the F. Mark Rafaty Memorial Award in nineteen ninety-four, the Larry Schoenrock Memorial Award in nineteen ninety-eight, and the Founders Club Lifetime Achievement Award in two thousand.

The doctor and his wife, Vicki, live in Key Biscayne. Their son, Matthew, is a resident at Mount Sinai Hospital and their daughter, Ilana, recently completed her doctorate in English at New York University.

the beauty makers
DR. SHELDON S. KABAKER
3324 Webster Street
Oakland, California 94601
(510) 451-1116

Dr. Sheldon S. Kabaker

hile in high school Dr. Sheldon S. Kabaker had to make a decision about his future, a difficult task for any young man. At the time he was working as a clerk, janitor, cashier and ran the camera department of his father's department store.

The decision he had to make was whether to go to college or continue working in retail sales at his father's store. The latter, obviously, would prepare him to take over the family business, which was tempting for a number of reasons.

The store offered tremendous security. It was an established business that required nothing more of him than continued on-the-job training. It was familiar, friendly territory, a comfort zone that required no dramatic change in lifestyle. He would be around people he knew and among friends with whom he had grown up. There would be the discipline of managing a business, of course, and the problems associated with it, presented a modest challenge. It would be a relatively easy lifestyle, which would certainly not require the all night preparation to get an "A" in a college exam.

But Dr. Kabaker, an Argo, Illinois native, was not all that interested in security. He was, in fact, motivated to explore new areas and opportunities. He was valedictorian of his high school class and it was quite obvious to his classmates that he loved learning and had an intense curiosity about the world around him. He also had an interest in working with people.

Once he fully realized that academics were his strong suit, he decided to go to college winning a scholarship to attend the University of Illinois. While in the academic world his attraction to science grew, so the decision to go to medical school was an easy one.

He went to the University of Illinois College of Medicine,

graduating in 1964. The young doctor then became a captain in the U.S. Army Medical Corps and served an internship at Letterman General Hospital in San Francisco, and later volunteered for duty in Vietnam for one year often treating combat wounds of the head and neck. Also, while in Vietnam, he worked with an American trained Vietnamese surgeon who did reconstructive work on the native population and developed a deepening interest in facial plastic surgery.

He returned to the United States and continued his surgical training in Otolarygology-Head and Neck Surgery at University Hospitals of Cleveland, Ohio, the Hines VA Hospital in Illinois and the Los Angeles County- University of Southern California Medical Center in L.A. Following this extensive postgraduate training, was a fellowship in facial plastic surgery studying under Dr. Richard Webster, a renowned plastic surgeon in Boston.

Dr. Kabaker has met rigorous requirements to become certified by the American Board of Otolaryngology, the American Board of Cosmetic Surgery and the American Board of Facial Plastic and Reconstructive Surgery. Only a handful of facial surgeons in the country hold these multiple credentials.

The doctor currently limits his practice to cosmetic surgery of the head and neck, which includes: hair restoration surgery, rhinoplasty, facial rejuvenation surgery and minimally invasive and non-surgical treatments for the aesthetic enhancement.

As one of the leading world authorities on hair replacement surgery, Dr. Kabaker writes and lectures extensively on the subject. He has been performing hair replacement work since 1963 and has the longest ongoing experience in the U.S. with what is known as the Juri flap operation. Dr. Kabaker has introduced the Juri flap and scalp expansion operations to numerous notable hair-transplant surgeons.

As one of the nation's leading experts in his field, he has been asked to serve in several professional and academic posts. He is currently an Associate Clinical Professor in the Department of Otolaryngology at the University of California-San Francisco School of Medicine, where he serves as a consultant in Facial Plastic Surgery.

He has also served on the board of directors of the American Academy of Facial Plastic and Reconstructive Surgery, The Foundation for Facial Plastic Surgery and the American Hair Loss Council. Additionally, he has served on the board of governors of the International Society of Hair Restoration Surgery for eight years and was its president in 1999.

Since 1985 Dr. Kabaker has been a fellowship director for the Educational Foundation of the American Academy of Facial Plastic and Reconstructive Surgery, training the top graduates of five-year head and neck surgery residency programs. He also has served as a surveyor for the California Medical Association's Ambulatory Care Accreditation Program. In addition to all of his other duties, he has been a member of the editorial board of Archives of Facial Plastic Surgery.

Since 1971 Dr. Kabaker has devoted an average of six weeks away from his practice each year participating in continuing medical education courses and meetings. He has studied plastic surgery in France, Spain, Italy, Mexico, Argentina and Australia. He has been the author of many textbook chapters and peer reviewed journal articles on subjects relative to facial plastic surgery. Dr. Kabaker lists over two hundred fifty lecture and course presentations he has given over his career.

His practice is housed in Oakland, California, at the Aesthetic Facial Plastic Surgery Medical Clinic, and offers outpatient aesthetic surgery at the fully equipped surgery center. The center has met nationally recognized standards for quality health care and is surveyed an accredited every three years. He said it offers a measure of privacy and cost effectiveness not possible in a hospital.

Though Dr. Kabaker stays very busy, he said he pushes himself to excel. He admires national and international leaders like Eisenhower and presently Colin Powell who exhibits strenth of their convictions yet used restraint in the face of adversity in the war and in peace.

"Yet my heroes are really those who more closely touched my life such as my first grade teacher, Julie Hay, who pioneered and passionately fought for the teaching of phonetics allowing her students, such as myself, to read at advanced levels. Also in this category is my father whose integrity led him to search 3 days for a customer in his store that was accidently overcharged by $2.00.

In the field of medicine people like my mentors Dr. Richard Webster of Boston, Massachusetts and Dr. Jack Anderson of New Orleans, Louisiana have greatly inspired him, he said.

"They inspired me with their philosophy of giving freely of one's acquired knowledge to the medical profession in exchange for the basic knowledge supplied by past teachers," he said.

The doctor said it is not a matter of just teaching others, but always learning and working hard to stay in the forefront of his profession.

Dr. Kabaker said he invests time in his local community, performing plastic surgery on victims of domestic violence and taking teaching cases in San Francisco at the University.

"The future looks bright for aesthetic surgery," he said. "With the advances in new surgical approaches leading to quicker healing and a speedy return to day to day activities, more and more people will have cosmetic surgery. It will be considered part of the natural order of life, almost a rite of passage.

"I enjoy the work. This is a happy business. I have no desire to retire as ongoing continuing experience makes for better results for my patients. I work to help people feel good about who they are. I've seen what a difference plastic surgery can make in someone's life."

the beauty makers

the beauty makers
RUSSELL W.H. KRIDEL, M.D.
6655 Travis #900
Houston, Texas 77030
(713) 526-5665

Dr. Russell Kridel

Dr. Russell Kridel, who established the charitable Face Foundation in Houston to help the battered victims of domestic violence by providing free reconstructive facial surgery, is a noted expert and lecturer in cosmetic primary rhinoplasty and nasal reconstruction following unsuccessful surgeries performed elsewhere or trauma. He is an innovator in face lift surgery and lectures extensively on how to do face lift surgery with inconspicuous incisions. He is also a recognized laser expert and has established the Cosmetic Laser Institute of Texas (in Houston), which houses five state-of-the-art lasers.

"We perform facial plastic surgery with the belief that a specialist can offer exceptional care in one area," the doctor said. "Our practice offers the patient a strong sense of security based on years of experience and thousands of successful outcomes.

"We perform rhinoplasty and nasal airway surgery, facial rejuvenation procedures including eyelid and face lifts, and facial implant surgery. With our state-of-the-art lasers, we perform skin resurfacing and rejuvenation surgery. In other words, we offer surgical excellence with an aesthetic and artistic perspective to help the individual's outward appearance reflect and amplify her or his inner vitality and beauty."

The Houston-based physician, who has testified before Congress on health care issues, is currently performing the largest ongoing study in the United States on the use of irradiated cartilage grafting in nasal reconstruction. He has been in private practice in Houston since 1981 and specializes in cosmetic surgery of the face and neck, with an emphasis on cosmetic and reconstructive rhinoplasty and aging face surgery.

"I do nose surgery on about one hundred fifty patients a year, whereas many doctors perform many fewer such surgeries," Dr.

Kridel said. "That's why it's important to ask the surgeon you're considering how many he or she does. If he or she does one or two per month, you should definitely compare his or her results with those of a doctor who does nose surgery frequently."

The doctor said that since the nose is not a beguiling feature, it's not at all surprising that improvements in this prominent feature are sought annually by thousands of Americans.

"When your nose is out of proportion with other features, it does seem to dominate the scene," he said. "That's why one of today's most sought-after cosmetic surgical procedures is the one that's intended to change the size and shape of the nose.

"In planning this type of surgery, I study the contour and shape of your face, your skin's texture and thickness, and your other features. Once I've done this, I have in mind a nose that suits your face and balances with your features. Then we sit down together, in front of a computer with imaging software, to establish a goal for surgery."

Dr. Kridel said that when a person sets out in search of information on the procedure, he or she may know little more than their goal – to make their nose smaller, narrower or wider.

"These are realistic goals," he said. "And, certainly, a good facial plastic surgeon can straighten a crooked nose, eliminate unsightly humps, reshape the tip, and improve the angle between the nose and upper lip. And if you're having trouble breathing, he can perform reconstructive procedures inside your nose to enhance airflow."

Dr. Kridel, of course, specializes in this procedure and has spearheaded many innovative nasal techniques. His publications on nasal surgery are often used as the basis for training new facial plastic surgeons. He is often asked to lecture on the subject at meetings attended by his peers – and his outstanding results and techniques draw doctors from all over the world to study with him (twenty have done fellowships with him in Houston). He has been on the invited faculty of every one of the American Academy of Facial Plastic & Reconstructive Surgery's advanced rhinoplasty courses for the last ten years.

Deformities inside the nose can impair breathing and cause

headaches or sinus trouble, the doctor said, but such problems can be corrected. He may remove excess bone or cartilage, or augment areas of the nose that lack enough bone or cartilage. Afterward he will reshape and rearrange remaining tissue and cartilage, fixing external and internal deformities.

"Occasionally a patient will bring in a movie-star photo to show me the type of nose they want," Dr. Kridel said. "But it's important not to confuse nose surgery with something like the shaping of clay. In performing a rhinoplasty, I'm operating with set criteria...the contour and shape of your face...the texture and thickness of your skin...the inclination of your chin, lips and forehead...the depth of angle between forehead and nose...your height...and the way your tissue heals.

"At times I suggest correcting a receding chin at the time of nose surgery to provide harmony of the facial features. And in the case of a nose that's very crooked, or one that has been injured, a second nose procedure may be necessary six months to a year later for further refinement."

Dr. Kridel is often called on to do "revision rhinoplasty" because the patient is not pleased with what another doctor did. A person who wants a revision is usually someone who has never been happy with her or his results, or who has had a hard time breathing ever since having the surgery. He also does revisions on noses that healed in an irregular manner and on noses that have an operated look because too much was removed.

"Looking at the psychological aspects of revision nose surgery," he said, "I've often found that one of the problems is not that something was technically wrong with the first surgery, but that the doctor actually failed to understand what the patient wanted. The failure to successfully communicate is often the primary problem.

"The goal with a revision is improvement rather than perfection. It's important that a patient understand that revision rhinoplasty is harder to perform than the first time around. Prior to the first surgery there are layers of tissue planes that have natural separations between the different types of nasal tissues and, as the surgeon operates, he can easily dissect or separate the layers to get to different structures. After a first surgery these planes no longer exist, making any subsequent surgery more difficult. It's almost as if someone has put glue in the nose because the skin is stuck to the cartilage and to the bone."

Dr. Kridel is also well known for his excellent work in face lift surgery. He feels face lifts should not be done unless the surgeon can hide the incisions well enough so it is hard for anyone to tell the patient had the procedure.

"Some doctors only address the neck and jowls and cheek and forget about the incisions, relying on the patient's hair to hide the incisions," he said. "I plan my face lifts so the patients can wear their hair up or back after surgery with no loss of hair or unsightly incisions showing."

Dr. Kridel does facial work exclusively, thus he has extensive experience in facial procedures such as nose surgery and face lifts. He understands not only aesthetics (the way the nose looks) but function, too.

He graduated Cum Laude from the Choate School and received his BA degree from Stanford University. Two years prior to graduating he spent six months in Florence, Italy studying art and history, during which time he became fascinated with various types of beauty throughout the ages. His interest in the standards of classic beauty led to his ambition to become a facial plastic surgeon.

In 1973 he was elected national president of the Student American Medical Association, and in 1975 received his MD from the University of Cincinnati College of Medicine. He then attended Baylor College of Medicine in Houston where he performed residencies in general surgery and then in otolaryngology (ear, nose and throat) – head and neck surgery. During his residency he coauthored a book on medical cost containment, which was published by the American Medical Association.

In 1981 he completed a fellowship in facial plastic surgery through the American Academy of Facial Plastic and Reconstructive Surgery under the direction of William K. Wright, MD.

Dr. Russell Kridel

Dr. Kridel was board-certified by the American Board of Otolaryngology (ABO) in 1981 and in 1984 became a Fellow of the American College of Surgeons. He has been a Fellowship Director for the American Academy of Facial Plastic and Reconstructive Surgery since 1985, and is responsible every year for the training of a Fellow in facial plastic surgery. He was certified by and became one of the first Fellows of the American Board of Facial Plastic and Reconstructive Surgery (ABFPRS) in 1991 and currently serves on the board of directors of the ABFPRS and is a board examiner in facial plastic surgery for both the ABO and ABFPRS.

The doctor holds faculty appointments at Baylor College of Medicine and at the University of Texas Health Science Center in Houston, and is on the medical staff of several hospitals. He just ended a three-year term as chief of staff of HealthSouth Hospital for Specialized Surgery.

In the fall of 2000 Dr. Kridel became national president of the American Academy of Facial Plastic and Reconstructive Surgery for one year, which he has also served as vice president for public affairs, treasurer, and as a member of the Executive Committee and Board of Directors. He is currently a facial plastic surgery delegate to the American Medical Association and is Harris County delegate to the Texas Medical Association. He served on the Ethics Committee of the Harris County Medical Society for three years.

A well-known speaker, he has given many lectures and courses on facial plastic surgery throughout the United States and in Italy, Mexico, Canada, Holland and Japan. He is one of the contributing authors of THE FACE BOOK, a patient's guide to facial plastic surgery published by the American Academy of Facial Plastic and Reconstructive surgery, and has also published more than sixty book chapters and scientific articles in medical journals.

Dr. Kridel is married to Cheryl Ann Kridel and they have two sons, Christopher and Blake. The couple are enthusiastic supporters of the theatre arts and he is a member of Houston's Alley's Theatre's Center Stage and the Alley Board of Directors.

glossary

ABDOMINAL ETCHING – Liposculpture of the abdomen in a physically fit male, which removes the fat that is smothering the abs and obliques.

ABDOMINOPLASTY – A plastic surgery procedure designed to tighten the abdominal skin and muscles. A variable amount of skin is generally removed below the belly button level with the skin incision normally hidden within the boundaries of a bikini or undergarment.

ALLODERM – These are sheets obtained from human organ donors, consisting of the deepest layers of skin containing no living cells, so they are not subject to transplant rejection or common infections. These sheets are processed according to guidelines of the U.S. Drug and Food Administration and the American Association of Tissue Banks. Placing this collagen under the skin replenishes the missing deep layers of skin, thereby elevating depressed scars or skin wrinkles. It can also be placed in the lips to make them appear larger. The material can last for more than two years without any visible loss of the collagen, but there are no guarantees as to how long the correction because of the insertion of this collagen will last. The edges of the sheet can be felt, but not usually seen for four to six weeks. After that there is in-growth into the material and the edges cannot be felt or seen.

AREOLA – A circular pigmented area surrounding the nipple of the breast.

BLEPHAROPLASTY – Plastic surgery of the eyelid usually involving removal of excess eyelid skin. This can be cosmetic or reconstructive in nature.

BLEPHAROPTOSIS – This is drooping of the upper eyelid. In normal forward gaze the edge of the upper eyelid should cover just the upper 2mm of the iris. Blepharoptosis exists if it lies lower.

BODY CONTOURING – This is the group of plastic surgery procedures used to change body contours. It includes ultrasonic body lift, abdominoplasty or tummy tuck, brachioplasty, liposuction, thigh buttock lifts, CAST liposuction, breast reduction and breast lift.

BOTOX – This is a compound produced to be bacteria, but it is not contagious or infectious. It temporarily paralyzes the muscles within three to five days following injection into the muscle. Results usually last between three and six months. The forehead, crows-feet, glabella and periorial areas can be treated with Botox.

BRACHIOPLASTY – This is plastic surgery performed on the upper arm to improve contours and give a straighter brachial border. It involves removal of skin on the inner aspect of the upper arm to tighten it, and usually involves liposuction to the area as well.

BROWLIFT – This is plastic surgery to raise the brow. It is achieved by placing incisions in the temporal area and at the hairline across the forehead to lift the upper third of the face.

CANTHOPLASTY-CANTHOPEXY – This surgery tightens the lower eyelid, which becomes lax as part of the aging process. When the laxity is severe the ligament is divided and a portion of the lower eyelid is removed before placing the suture, a canthopexy.

CAPSULE – This is an anatomical structure in which something is enclosed, such as a breast implant. When a breast implant is placed in the body, the body attempts to wall it off, forming a capsule around the implant. This capsule can be present within a week after surgery and is eventually present in all breasts containing implants.

CAPSULECTOMY – This is surgical removal of the breast

implant capsule.

CAST LIPOSUCTION – This is Circumferential para-Axillary Superficial Tumescent liposuction, a procedure for arm Liposculpture to prevent and treat the batwing deformity. The goal is to create regional harmony with body fat reduction in the arm, lateral breast, armpit and upper back.

CELLULITE – This word is used to describe the uneven pitted surface or dimpling of the skin commonly seen on the thighs of women.

CHEMICAL PEEL – This is use of a chemical exfoliative on the skin surface to treat facial wrinkles. The surface layer of the skin is sloughed in seven to nine days, giving a fresh appearance to the skin.

COLLAGEN – Injectable collagen is derived from cow skin. It is commonly injected under the skin surface to lighten or erase facial wrinkles or acne scars, or to make the Vermillion border more prominent. The material is slowly degraded so that the results of injection last at most three to six months. Regular injections are required to maintain the results.

COLUMELLA – This is the vertical bridge of skin between the nostrils. On side view the aesthetic position of the skin edge of the columella should be 4mm below the outer rim of the nostril.

CONTRACTURE – This is the effect seen of scar tissue contracting upon itself. After placement of breast implants the capsule can contract around and squeeze the implant into a tight, hard, round mass, thus the name capsular contracture.

COSMETIC SURGERY – This is surgery performed to enhance normal structures of the body to make them look better or different.

glossary

DERMABRASION – This is abrasion of the skin surface performed using an apparatus with a wire brush, sandpaper like material or other rough surface, whereas the outermost layers of the skin or abraded or rubbed away. After the area heals the skin is smoother and may be lighter in color. This process is commonly used on facial acne scars and aging wrinkles of the lips.

DERMATOCHALASIS – This is the presence of excess eyelid skin, which contributes to the appearance of upper and lower eyelid bags. In the upper eyelids the bags seen are usually some combination of dermatochalasis that is treated by blepharoplasty and brow drooping, which is treated by browlift.

DORSAL HUMP – This refers to the bump on or prominence of the nasal bridge. This dorsal hump is usually taken down during Rhinoplasty surgery.

EDEMA – This is the medical term for swelling, an accumulation of an excessive amount of fluid in cells and tissues.

FACELIFT – This is a term used to describe the surgical procedure whereby an incision is made vertically down the temple, extended downward just in front of the ear and then brought up the backside of the ear. The skin is then dissected free from underlying structures towards the center of the face. Excess skin is excised from the margin of the incision and then the skin edges are sutured together. The result is the removal of excess skin, especially of the neck, and less so of the cheek and lower face. Another term for the procedure is Facialplasty.

FACIAL LIPOSUCTION AND BUCCAL FAT PAD EXCISION – In individuals with round cheeks a more sculpted look is achieved with removal of "buccal fat." This fat pad is approximately the size of a golf ball and sits next to the lining of the mouth. The removal of this fat pad lessens facial roundness. Through a small incision inside the mouth this fat is easily extracted to provide more definition to the cheekbone and creates a slight hollowness resulting in better definition. This is especially effective when combined with conservative facial liposuction. The cheek fold, jowls and sagging neck are the most common areas treated with facial liposuction and can be effectively reduced.

FACIAL LIPOSUCTION WITH NECK TIGHTENING (PLATYMAPLASTY) – This procedure treats the sagging neck due to fat accumulation above and below the thin neck muscles called platysma. Best results occur with conservative debulking of fat with tightening of the neck muscles in an attempt to diminish the appearance of these unsightly bands. This is not a substitute for facelift, but effectively reduces scarring and improves the contour of the face and neck.

FASCIA – This is a thin sheet of fibrous tissue that envelope the body beneath the skin and also encloses muscles or groups of muscles. At the far end of muscles fascia coalesces to become the outermost layers of tendons.

FAT GRAFTING – This involves taking fat from one area, usually obtained by liposuction, and injecting it in another area. The grafts have variable and unpredictable amounts of resorption so that as many as three to six injections may be required to achieve a desired result.

FOREHEADPLASTY – This is the same procedure as Browlift, but can include reshaping of the forehead bone. Boney ridges or bossing of the forehead can be shaved down to give a more feminine facial appearance.

GENIOPLASTY – This is a surgical procedure to change the shape of the chin bone by cutting the bone and changing its position.

Genioplasty refers to surgery where the chin bone is actually cut, as opposed to chin augmentation with an implant where it is not.

GIGANTO VOLUME LIPOSUCTION – This refers to more than twenty pounds of fat removal.

GYNECOMASTIA – This refers to enlargement of the male breast, which is most common around puberty and can be unilateral or bilateral. Most commonly the enlargement is centralized in the breast.

HEMATOMA – This is a collection of blood outside the blood vessels, but still confined within the tissues or organs of the body. This blood is usually completely or partly clotted. Such complication can arise after any surgery, especially if the patient is on blood thinners, or after a traumatic injury. All large hematomas should be surgically drained, especially those under skin elevated in a facelift, breast reduction or abdominoplasty. Ignoring expanding hematomas in such settings can lead to the death of the overlying skin and poor cosmetic result. Small hematomas can be absorbed by the body, or aspirated with syringe and needle after the hematoma liquefies.

HYDROQUINONE – This is the active ingredient in most skin bleaching creams. Hydroquinone inhibits the production of skin pigmentation without causing permanent damage to the cells that produce the pigment.

HYPERTROPHIC SCAR – This is a ridge or string-like segment of scar seem within the confines of the original wound.

INFRACTURE – This is the term used to describe the part of nasal surgery where the nasal bones are moved inward to narrow the nasal bridge.

KELOID – These are large, sometimes dumbbell-shaped, scars that grow out of the confines of the original wound.

LARGE VOLUME LIPOSUCTION – This refers to up to twelve pounds of fat removal.

LIPOMA – This is a benign tumor composed of fat cells. There are at least three types of benign lipomas. One is reported to occur after localized trauma, appears as a single lipoma and is very slow growing. Another is an angiolipoma, which tends to occur in multiple areas all over the body and has more blood vessels within it, is due to a genetic predisposition and grows even more slowly. Another rare form occurs within muscles and is even less well understood. Though lipomas are benign they can cause problems if they grow to sufficient size to compress adjacent structures such as nerves and arteries.

LIPOSUCTION – This is the surgical removal of fat using a hollow tube (cannula) connected to negative pressure to aspirate the fat from under the skin. The goal is to create a marked reduction in size with smooth skin.

LOCAL ANESTHESIA – This is the form of anesthesia most commonly used for small surgical procedures. The area is injected with anesthetic much the same way as a dentist injects the mouth to work on teeth. The protective reflexes are not hampered; blood pressure, heart rate and other vital signs do not need to be monitored; and the patient remains fully awake during the procedure.

LYMPH EDEMA – This is swelling due to obstruction or destruction of lymphatic vessels or lymph nodes. Lymph is a clear fluid containing protein and white blood cells. It flows back from the extremities in lymph vessels and mixes with vein blood near the heart. After passing through the heart and lungs it travels back to the extremities in arteries. Treatment for lymph edema is compression garment application and deep massage to facilitate flow in the lymphatic vessels. Lymph nodes are nodules present in certain parts of the lymphatic vessels. They are site of white blood cell replication.

MALAR POUCHES – This refers to puffiness or bulges over the cheekbones separate from the eyelids. In some cases fat deep to the part of the eyelid muscle below the lid itself herniates through the muscle to a more superficial position and is visible from the outside as a pouch. This can be treated by liposuction, as it is not yet eyelid fat.

MAMMOPLASTY – This is any plastic surgery procedure performed on the breast.

MARIONETTE LINES – This refers to lines of aging or skin folds on either side of the chin and in front of the jowls. These lines are caused by the presence of a ligament between the skin in this area and underlying deeper structures. As adjacent skin descends with the process of aging, the skin directly over the ligament stays in place creating this fold.

MASTOPLEXY – This is plastic surgery performed to lift the sagging breast.

MEDIAL THIGH LIFT – This involves removing inner upper thigh skin. The incision is hidden in the crease where the inner thigh meets the torso.

MEDIUM VOLUME LIPOSUCTION – This is up to six pounds of fat removal.

MEGA VOLUME LIPOSUCTION – This is up to twenty pounds of fat removed.

MENTALIS STRAIN – This is dimpling of the chin skin seen when the lips are touching. It is caused by a retruded or small chin and the need for the chin muscles to strain in order for the upper and lower lips to touch. The treatment is to place a chin implant.

MICROGENIA – This refers to a small chin, which can be corrected with placement of a chin implant.

MID-FACELIFT – Sometimes referred to as the vertical facelift, this procedure furnishes additional rejuvenating properties by blunting the contrast between the lower eyelid margin and cheek, and by making the skin folds between the corners of the nose and mouth shallower.

MILIA – This is a small whitish cyst close to the skin surface. It consists of skin surface cells that have been driven down to a deeper level and have been walled off, as they are considered foreign in this position. This can occur after any surgical or traumatic injury to the skin. The cyst is unroofed with a small needle and the contents released. This heals without scarring and reoccurrence is rare.

MODIFIED ADDOMINAL ETCHING – This is a form of liposuction designed to enhance the vertical aesthetic shadows of the abdomen for the active male in less-than-perfect condition or females in their perfect condition.

MOLE – These are brown-pigmented areas on the skin that can be a number of things: benign (aging spots, scars, old or chronic collection of blood under the skin from venous stasis or after traumatic, seborrheic keratosis, freckles, melasma, moles or nevi) or malignant (basal cell carcinoma, melanoma). They can be congenital or arise later in life.

NASOLABIAL FOLD – This is the term for skin folds between the corners of the nose and mouth.

glossary

OTOPLASTY – This is plastic surgery of the ear.

PIXY EARS – This refers to lack of a true earlobe. The lower portion of the ear extends straight out from the side of the head without a free hanging earlobe.

PLATYSMAL BANDS – These are the vertical edges of the neck platysmal muscle. The paired bands are seen on the front of the neck to either side of the midline. Their visibility is a common aspect of the aging process. Surgical lifting of the midface-check fat early on can adequately treat these bands. In more advanced cases the overlying skin is elevated and the bands sutured together during face or neck surgery.

POST INFLAMMATORY HYPERPIGMENTATION – This refers to darkening of skin in darker complexion individuals following skin surface damage. It usually appears four to six weeks after injury.

PRIMARY SURGERY – This is the first time a surgical procedure is performed; for example, primary rhinoplasty as opposed to secondary rhinoplasty. The former would be the first nasal surgery and the latter would be later operations to correct the first surgery, or to make additional changes to the nose.

RECONSTRUCTIVE SURGERY – This is surgery performed to correct or repair abnormal structures of the body caused by congenital defects, developmental abnormalities, trauma, injection, tumors or disease so as to improve function or create a normal appearance to the extent possible. By law these procedures must be covered by health insurance carriers.

REDUCTION MAMMOPLASTY – This is breast reduction surgery.

RHINOPLASTY – This is surgery to reshape the nose, and one of the most common of all plastic surgery procedures. It can reduce or increase the size of the nose, change the shape of the tip or bridge, narrow the span of the nostrils, or change the angle between the nose and upper lip. It may also correct a birth defect or injury, or help relieve breathing problems.

SCAR – This is the result of the skin repairing wounds caused by accident, disease or surgical incision, and is an essential part of the body's healing process.

SEPTAL DEVIATION – The nose is comprised of two nasal airways divided by the nasal septum. When the nasal septum is crooked (deviated septum) it can block the free flow of air through the nose and block drainage of the sinuses, which drain through the outer walls into the nose.

SKIN TAGS – These are benign overgrowths of skin that protrude outward from the skin in mushroom-like fashion. They can occur virtually anywhere you have skin, but are easily removed under local anesthetic.

SMALL VOLUME LIPOSUCTION – This refers to up to three pounds of fat removal.

SOFTFORM – This is a tubular implant made of expanded polytetrafluoroethylenne housed in a sterile insertion trocar apparatus. The material is placed under the facial skin for the reduction of deep furrows or enhancement of vermilion border definition.

STRETCHMARKS – collagen fibers under the skin surface break when overstretched. The result is atrophy of the deeper dermal layers of the skin and a grossly visible stretch mark. Large underlying muscles or accumulations of fat can cause this stretching. Stretch marks are commonly seen on the abdominal skin of women after childbirth. The only way to get rid of them is removal of the involved skin as in an abdominoplasty/tummy tuck or thigh-buttock lift.

THIGH/BUTTOCK LIFT – The thigh and buttock skin is re-elevated by removing a section of skin that lies under what is normally covered by underwear or a bathing suit. The removal is performed circumferentially.

TRADITIONAL LIPOSUCTION – This is removal of four to six pounds of localized fat by simply reducing the convexities of the body, primarily abdomen, hips and outer thighs. It typically results in more blood loss, more bruising, slow recovery and the need for a blood transfusion if the four- to six-pound limit is exceeded.

TUBEROUS BREASTS – The skin of the lower half of the breast remains attached to the chest wall and does not grow with the remainder of the breast during puberty. The result is a breast with less tissue below the nipple than above it and a high infra-breast skin crease. The developing tissue in some cases may be forced into, or herniate into, the darker tissue surrounding the breast nipple (areola) and may be constricted at its base. This may occur in one or both breasts. The treatment involves correction of the hernia if present, release of the constricted base and lowering of the attachment of the breast to the chest wall with or without placement of a breast implant.

TUMESCENT LIPOSUCTION – Tissues are infiltrated with a high volume of fluid and the fat suctioned out under general anesthesia via incisions hidden in skin creases.

ULTRASOUND ASSISTED LIPOSUCTION – A probe is placed under the skin and into the fat to surgically disintegrate it, facilitating its removal.

VERMILLION BORDER – This is the border between skin of the lip and the area where lipstick is normally worn.

Note: This glossary is not complete, but most doctors profiled in this book have websites that give complete details of most plastic surgery procedures. It is recommended that anyone considering a procedure carefully study the ample information about it, which can be readily accessed in libraries and on the World Wide Web.